Glencoe McGraw-Hill

Chapter 6 Resource Masters

Algebra 2

$^2 = 0$

$= -0.5x^2$

O

x

Mc Graw Hill Glencoe

CONSUMABLE WORKBOOKS Many of the worksheets contained in the Chapter Resource Masters are available as consumable workbooks in both English and Spanish.

	ISBN10	ISBN13
Study Guide and Intervention Workbook	0-07-890861-2	978-0-07-890861-3
Homework Practice Workbook	0-07-890862-0	978-0-07-890862-0

Spanish Version

Homework Practice Workbook	0-07-890866-3	978-0-07-890866-8

Answers For Workbooks The answers for Chapter 6 of these workbooks can be found in the back of this Chapter Resource Masters booklet.

StudentWorks Plus™ This CD-ROM includes the entire Student Edition test along with the English workbooks listed above.

TeacherWorks Plus™ All of the materials found in this booklet are included for viewing, printing, and editing in this CD-ROM.

Spanish Assessment Masters (ISBN10: 0-07-890869-8, ISBN13: 978-0-07-890869-9)
These masters contain a Spanish version of Chapter 6 Test Form 2A and Form 2C.

The McGraw-Hill Companies

 Glencoe

Copyright © by The McGraw-Hill Companies, Inc. All rights reserved. Permission is granted to reproduce the material contained herein on the condition that such materials be reproduced only for classroom use; be provided to students, teachers, and families without charge; and be used solely in conjunction with the *Glencoe Algebra2* program. Any other reproduction, for sale or other use, is expressly prohibited.

Send all inquiries to:
Glencoe/McGraw-Hill
8787 Orion Place
Columbus, OH 43240-4027

ISBN: 978-0-07-890531-5
MHID: 0-07-890531-1

Printed in the United States of America.

1 2 3 4 5 6 7 8 9 10 045 14 13 12 11 10 09 08

Contents

Teacher's Guide to Using the
Chapter 6 Resource Masters

The *Chapter 6 Resource Masters* includes the core materials needed for Chapter 6. These materials include worksheets, extensions, and assessment options. The answers for these pages appear at the back of this booklet.

All of the materials found in this booklet are included for viewing and printing on the *TeacherWorks Plus*™ CD-ROM.

Chapter Resources

Student-Built Glossary (pages 1–2) These masters are a student study tool that presents up to twenty of the key vocabulary terms from the chapter. Students are to recording definitions and/or examples for each term. You may suggest that student highlight or star the terms with which they are not familiar. Give to students before beginning Lesson 6-1. Encourage them to add these ages to their mathematics study notebooks. Remind them to complete the appropriate words as they study each lesson.

Anticipation Guide (pages 3–4) This master presented in both English and Spanish is a survey used before beginning the chapter to pinpoint what students may or may not know about the concepts in the chapter. Students will revisit this survey after they complete the chapter to see if their perceptions have changed.

Lesson Resources

Study Guide and Intervention These masters provide vocabulary, key concepts, additional worked-out examples and Check Your Progress exercises to use as a reteaching activity. It can also be used in conjunction with the Student Edition as an instructional tool for students who have been absent.

Skills Practice This master focuses more on the computational nature of the lesson. Use as an additional practice option or as homework for second-day teaching of the lesson.

Practice This master closely follows the types of problems found in the Exercises section of the Student Edition and includes word problems. Use as an additional practice option or as homework for second-day teaching of the lesson.

Word Problem Practice This master includes additional practice in solving word problems that apply the concepts of the lesson. Use as an additional practice or as homework for second-day teaching of the lesson.

Enrichment These activities may extend the concepts of the lesson, offer an historical or multicultural look at the concepts, or widen students' perspectives on the mathematics they are learning. They are written for use with all levels of students.

Graphing Calculator, TI–NSpire, or *Spreadsheet Activities* These activities present ways in which technology can be used with the concepts in some lessons of this chapter. Use as an alternative approach to some concepts or as an integral part of your lesson presentation.

Assessment Options

The assessment masters in the *Chapter 6 Resource Masters* offer a wide range of assessment tools for formative (monitoring) assessment and summative (final) assessment.

Student Recording Sheet This master corresponds with the standardized test practice at the end of the chapter.

Extended Response Rubric This master provides information for teachers and students on how to assess performance on open-ended questions.

Quizzes Four free-response quizzes offer assessment at appropriate intervals in the chapter.

Mid-Chapter Test This 1-page test provides an option to assess the first half of the chapter. It parallels the timing of the Mid-Chapter Quiz in the Student Edition and includes both multiple-choice and free-response questions.

Vocabulary Test This test is suitable for all students. It includes a list of vocabulary words and 10 questions to assess students' knowledge of those words. This can also be used in conjunction with one of the leveled chapter tests.

Leveled Chapter Tests

- *Form 1* contains multiple-choice questions and is intended for use with below grade level students.
- *Forms 2A and 2B* contain multiple-choice questions aimed at on grade level students. These tests are similar in format to offer comparable testing situations.

- *Forms 2C and 2D* contain free-response questions aimed at on grade level students. These tests are similar in format to offer comparable testing situations.
- *Form 3* is a free-response test for use with above grade level students.

All of the above mentioned tests include a free-response Bonus question.

Extended-Response Test Performance assessment tasks are suitable for all students. Sample answers and a scoring rubric are included for evaluation.

Standardized Test Practice These three pages are cumulative in nature. It includes three parts: multiple-choice questions with bubble-in answer format, griddable questions with answer grids, and short-answer free-response questions.

Answers

- The answers for the Anticipation Guide and Lesson Resources are provided as reduced pages.
- Full-size answer keys are provided for the assessment masters.

6 Student-Built Glossary

This is an alphabetical list of the key vocabulary terms you will learn in Chapter 6. As you study the chapter, complete each term's definition or description. Remember to add the page number where you found the term. Add these pages to your Algebra Study Notebook to review vocabulary at the end of the chapter.

Vocabulary Term	Found on Page	Definition/Description/Example
degree of a polynomial		
depressed polynomial		
end behavior		
extrema		
leading coefficient		
polynomial function		
polynomial in one variable		
power function		

(continued on the next page)

6 Student-Built Glossary *(continued)*

Vocabulary Term	Found on Page	Definition/Description/Example
prime polynomials		
quadratic form		
relative maximum		
relative minimum		
simplify		
synthetic division		
synthetic substitution		
turning points		

6 Anticipation Guide

Polynomials and Polynomial Functions

Step 1 — *Before you begin Chapter 6*

- Read each statement.
- Decide whether you Agree (A) or Disagree (D) with the statement.
- Write A or D in the first column OR if you are not sure whether you agree or disagree, write NS (Not Sure).

STEP 1 A, D, or NS	Statement	STEP 2 A or D
	1. The monomial $6m^4n^2p^5$ has a degree of 5.	
	2. To multiply powers of the same variable, add the exponents.	
	3. $(12t^2 - 3t + 4) - (8t^2 + 4t - 4)$ is equal to $4t^2 - 7t + 8$.	
	4. $(6x + 2)(7x - 1)$ is equal to $42x^2 - 2$.	
	5. The *leading coefficient* of a polynomial is the coefficient of the first term.	
	6. The graph of any polynomial is a parabola.	
	7. The graph of a polynomial of even degree will approach either $+\infty$ or $-\infty$ as $x \rightarrow +\infty$ and as $x \rightarrow -\infty$.	
	8. If the graph of a polynomial function has an x-intercept, then the polynomial has at least one real solution.	
	9. $a^2 - 2ab - b^2$ is a perfect square trinomial.	
	10. If $f(a) = 0$, then $x - a$ is a factor of the polynomial $f(x)$.	
	11. Every polynomial equation with degree greater than 0 has at least one root in the set of complex numbers.	
	12. To find all the rational zeros of a polynomial function, all the possible zeros must be tested using synthetic substitution.	

Step 2 — *After you complete Chapter 6*

- Reread each statement and complete the last column by entering an A or a D.
- Did any of your opinions about the statements change from the first column?
- For those statements that you mark with a D, use a piece of paper to write an example of why you disagree.

6   Ejercicios preparatorios

Polinomios y funciones polinómicas

Paso 1   *Antes de comenzar el Capítulo 6*

- Lee cada enunciado.

- Decide si estás de acuerdo (A) o en desacuerdo (D) con el enunciado.

- Escribe A o D en la primera columna O si no estás seguro(a) de la respuesta, escribe NS (No estoy seguro(a)).

PASO 1 A, D o NS	Enunciado	PASO 2 A o D
	1. El monomio $6m^4n^2p^5$ tiene un grado de 5.	
	2. Para multiplicar potencias de la misma variable, suma los exponentes.	
	3. $(12t^2 - 3t + 4) - (8t^2 + 4t - 4)$ es igual a $4t^2 - 7t + 8$.	
	4. $(6x + 2)(7x - 1)$ es igual a $42x^2 - 2$.	
	5. El *coeficiente principal* de un polinomio es el coeficiente del primer término.	
	6. La gráfica de cualquier polinomio es una parábola.	
	7. La gráfica del polinomio de grado par se aproximará a $+\infty$ o $-\infty$ a medida que $x \to +\infty$ y a medida que $x \to -\infty$.	
	8. Si la gráfica de una función de polinomios tiene una intersección x, entonces el polinomio tiene por lo menos una solución real.	
	9. $a^2 - 2ab - b^2$ es un trinomio perfecto al cuadrado.	
	10. Si $f(a) = 0$, entonces $x - a$ es un factor del polinomio $f(x)$.	
	11. Cada ecuación polinomial con un grado mayor que 0 tiene por lo menos una raíz en el conjunto de números complejos.	
	12. Para encontrar todos los ceros racionales de una función polinomial, deben probarse todos los ceros posibles utilizando sustitución sintética.	

Paso 2   *Después de completar el Capítulo 6*

- Vuelve a leer cada enunciado y completa la última columna con una A o una D.

- ¿Cambió cualquiera de tus opiniones sobre los enunciados de la primera columna?

- En una hoja de papel aparte, escribe un ejemplo de por qué estás en desacuerdo con los enunciados que marcaste con una D.

6-1 Study Guide and Intervention

Operations with Polynomials

Multiply and Divide Monomials **Negative exponents** are a way of expressing the multiplicative inverse of a number.

Negative Exponents	$a^{-n} = \dfrac{1}{a^n}$ and $\dfrac{1}{a^{-n}} = a^n$ for any real number $a \neq 0$ and any integer n.

When you **simplify an expression**, you rewrite it without powers of powers, parentheses, or negative exponents. Each base appears only once, and all fractions are in simplest form. The following properties are useful when simplifying expressions.

Product of Powers	$a^m \cdot a^n = a^{m+n}$ for any real number a and integers m and n.
Quotient of Powers	$\dfrac{a^m}{a^n} = a^{m-n}$ for any real number $a \neq 0$ and integers m and n.
Properties of Powers	For a, b real numbers and m, n integers: $(a^m)^n = a^{mn}$ $(ab)^m = a^m b^m$ $\left(\dfrac{a}{b^n}\right) = \dfrac{a^n}{b^n}, b \neq 0$ $\left(\dfrac{a}{b}\right)^{-n} = \left(\dfrac{b}{a}\right)^n$ or $\dfrac{b^n}{a^n}, a \neq 0, b \neq 0$

Example Simplify. Assume that no variable equals 0.

a. $(3m^4 n^{-2})(-5mn)^2$

$(3m^4 n^{-2})(-5mn)^2 = 3m^4 n^{-2} \cdot 25m^2 n^2$
$= 75m^4 m^2 n^{-2} n^2$
$= 75m^{4+2} n^{-2+2}$
$= 75m^6$

b. $\dfrac{(-m^4)^3}{(2m^2)^{-2}}$

$\dfrac{(-m^4)^3}{(2m^2)^{-2}} = \dfrac{-m^{12}}{\frac{1}{4m^4}}$
$= -m^{12} \cdot 4m^4$
$= -4m^{16}$

Exercises

Simplify. Assume that no variable equals 0.

1. $c^{12} \cdot c^{-4} \cdot c^6$

2. $\dfrac{b^8}{b^2}$

3. $(a^4)^5$

4. $\dfrac{x^{-2}y}{x^4 y^{-1}}$

5. $\left(\dfrac{a^2 b}{a^{-3} b^2}\right)^{-1}$

6. $\left(\dfrac{x^2 y}{xy^3}\right)^2$

7. $\dfrac{1}{2}(-5a^2 b^3)^2 (abc)^2$

8. $m^7 \cdot m^8$

9. $\dfrac{8m^3 n^2}{4mn^3}$

10. $\dfrac{2^3 c^4 t^2}{2^2 c^4 t^2}$

11. $4j(-j^{-2} k^2)(3j^3 k^{-7})$

12. $\dfrac{2mn^2 (3m^2 n)^2}{12m^3 n^4}$

6-1 Study Guide and Intervention *(continued)*

Operations with Polynomials

Operations with Polynomials

Polynomial	a monomial or a sum of monomials
Like Terms	terms that have the same variable(s) raised to the same power(s)

To add or subtract polynomials, perform the indicated operations and combine like terms.

Example 1 Simplify $4xy^2 + 12xy - 7x^2y - (20xy \quad 5xy^2 - 8x^2y)$.

$4xy^2 + 12xy - 7x^2y - (20xy + 5xy^2 - 8x^2y)$

$= 4xy^2 + 12xy - 7x^2y - 20xy - 5xy^2 + 8x^2y$ Distribute the minus sign.

$= (-7x^2y + 8x^2y) + (4xy^2 - 5xy^2) + (12xy - 20xy)$ Group like terms.

$= x^2y - xy^2 - 8xy$ Combine like terms.

You use the distributive property when you multiply polynomials. When multiplying binomials, the **FOIL** pattern is helpful.

FOIL Pattern	To multiply two binomials, add the products of
	F the *first* terms, **O** the *outer* terms, **I** the *inner* terms, and **L** the *last* terms.

Example 2 Find $(6x - 5)(2x + 1)$.

$(6x - 5)(2x + 1) = \quad 6x \cdot 2x \quad + \quad 6x \cdot 1 \quad + \quad (-5) \cdot 2x \quad + \quad (-5) \cdot 1$

            First terms   Outer terms   Inner terms   Last terms

$= 12x^2 + 6x - 10x - 5$ Multiply monomials.

$= 12x^2 - 4x - 5$ Add like terms.

Exercises

Simplify.

1. $(6x^2 - 3x + 2) - (4x^2 + x - 3)$ **2.** $(7y^2 + 12xy - 5x^2) + (6xy - 4y^2 - 3x^2)$

3. $(-4m^2 - 6m) - (6m + 4m^2)$ **4.** $27x^2 - 5y^2 + 12y^2 - 14x^2$

5. $\frac{1}{4}x^2 - \frac{3}{8}xy + \frac{1}{2}y^2 - \frac{1}{2}xy + \frac{1}{4}y^2 - \frac{3}{8}x^2$ **6.** $24p^3 - 15p^2 + 3p - 15p^3 + 13p^2 - 7p$

Find each product.

7. $2x(3x^2 - 5)$ **8.** $7a(6 - 2a - a^2)$

9. $(x^2 - 2)(x^2 - 5)$ **10.** $(x + 1)(2x^2 - 3x + 1)$

11. $(2n^2 - 3)(n^2 + 5n - 1)$ **12.** $(x - 1)(x^2 - 3x + 4)$

6-1 Skills Practice

Operations with Polynomials

Simplify. Assume that no variable equals 0.

1. $b^4 \cdot b^3$

2. $c^5 \cdot c^2 \cdot c^2$

3. $a^{-4} \cdot a^{-3}$

4. $x^5 \cdot x^{-4} \cdot x$

5. $(2x)^2(4y)^2$

6. $-2gh(g^3h^5)$

7. $10x^2y^3(10xy^8)$

8. $\dfrac{24wz^7}{3w^3z^5}$

9. $\dfrac{-6a^4bc^8}{36a^7b^2c}$

10. $\dfrac{-10pt^4r}{-5p^3t^2r}$

11. $(g + 5) + (2g + 7)$

12. $(5d + 5) - (d + 1)$

13. $(x^2 - 3x - 3) + (2x^2 + 7x - 2)$

14. $(-2f^2 - 3f - 5) + (-2f^2 - 3f + 8)$

15. $-5(2c^2 - d^2)$

16. $x^2(2x + 9)$

17. $(a - 5)^2$

18. $(2x - 3)(3x - 5)$

19. $(r - 2t)(r + 2t)$

20. $(3y + 4)(2y - 3)$

21. $(3 - 2b)(3 + 2b)$

22. $(3w + 1)^2$

6-1 Practice

Operations with Polynomials

Simplify. Assume that no variable equals 0.

1. $n^5 \cdot n^2$

2. $y^7 \cdot y^3 \cdot y^2$

3. $t^9 \cdot t^{-8}$

4. $x^{-4} \cdot x^{-4} \cdot x^4$

5. $(2f^4)^6$

6. $(-2b^{-2}c^3)^3$

7. $(4d^2t^5v^{-4})(-5dt^{-3}v^{-1})$

8. $8u(2z)^3$

9. $\dfrac{12m^8y^6}{-9my^4}$

10. $\dfrac{-6s^5x^3}{18sx^7}$

11. $\dfrac{-27x^3(-x^7)}{16x^4}$

12. $\left(\dfrac{2}{3r^2s^3z^6}\right)^2$

13. $-(4w^{-3}z^{-5})(8w)^2$

14. $(m^4n^6)^4(m^3n^2p^5)^6$

15. $\left(\dfrac{3}{2}d^-f^4\right)^4\left(-\dfrac{4}{3}d^5f\right)^3$

16. $\left(\dfrac{2x^3y^2}{-x^2y^5}\right)^{-2}$

17. $\dfrac{(3x^{-2}y^3)(5xy^{-8})}{(x^{-3})^4y^{-2}}$

18. $\dfrac{-20(m^2v)(-v)^3}{5(-v)^2(-m^4)}$

19. $(3n^2 + 1) + (8n^2 - 8)$

20. $(6w - 11w^2) - (4 + 7w^2)$

21. $(w + 2t)(w^2 - 2wt + 4t^2)$

22. $(x + y)(x^2 - 3xy + 2y^2)$

23. BANKING Terry invests $1500 in two mutual funds. The first year, one fund grows 3.8% and the other grows 6%. Write a polynomial to represent the amount Terry's $1500 grows to in that year if x represents the amount he invested in the fund with the lesser growth rate.

24. GEOMETRY The area of the base of a rectangular box measures $2x^2 + 4x - 3$ square units. The height of the box measures x units. Find a polynomial expression for the volume of the box.

6-1   Word Problem Practice

Operations with Polynomials

1. THE EARTH   Earth's diameter is approximately 1.2756×10^4 kilometers. The surface area of a sphere can be found using the formula $SA = 4\pi r^2$.

1.2756 × 10⁴ km

What is the approximate surface area of Earth?

2. VOLUME   The volume of a rectangular prism is given by the product of its length, width, and height. Samantha has a rectangular prism that has a length of b^2 units, a width of a units, and a height of $ab + c$ units.

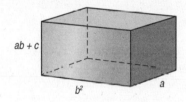

$ab + c$

b^2 a

What is the volume of Samantha's rectangular prism? Express your answer in simplified form.

3. CONSTRUCTION   A rectangular deck is built around a square pool. The pool has side length s. The length of the deck is 5 units longer than twice the side length of the pool. The width of the deck is 3 units longer than the side length of the pool. What is the area of the deck in terms of s?

4. SAIL BOATS   Tamara requests a custom-made sail for her sailboat. The base of her triangular sail is $2x + 1$ and the height is $4x + 6$.

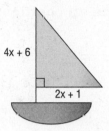

$4x + 6$

$2x + 1$

a. Find the area of the sail.

b. If Tamara wants a different fabric on each side of her sail, write a polynomial to represent the total amount of fabric she will need to make the sail.

c. Tamara decides she also wants a special trim for the hypotenuse of her triangular sail. Write an expression that describes the amount of trim she will need.

6-1 Enrichment

Polynomials with Fractional Coefficients

Polynomials may have fractional coefficients as long as there are no variables in the denominators. Computing with fractional coefficients is performed in the same way as computing with whole-number coefficients.

Simplify. Write all coefficients as fractions.

1. $\left(\frac{3}{5}m - \frac{2}{7}p - \frac{1}{3}n\right) - \left(\frac{7}{3}p - \frac{5}{2}m - \frac{3}{4}n\right)$

2. $\left(\frac{3}{2}x - \frac{4}{3}y - \frac{5}{4}z\right) + \left(-\frac{1}{4}x + y + \frac{2}{5}z\right) + \left(-\frac{7}{8}x - \frac{6}{7}y + \frac{1}{2}z\right)$

3. $\left(\frac{1}{2}a^2 - \frac{1}{3}ab + \frac{1}{4}b^2\right) + \left(\frac{5}{6}a^2 + \frac{2}{3}ab - \frac{3}{4}b^2\right)$

4. $\left(\frac{1}{2}a^2 - \frac{1}{3}ab + \frac{1}{4}b^2\right) - \left(\frac{1}{3}a^2 - \frac{1}{2}ab + \frac{5}{6}b^2\right)$

5. $\left(\frac{1}{2}a^2 - \frac{1}{3}ab + \frac{1}{4}b^2\right) \cdot \left(\frac{1}{2}a - \frac{2}{3}b\right)$

6. $\left(\frac{2}{3}a^2 - \frac{1}{5}a + \frac{2}{7}\right) \cdot \left(\frac{2}{3}a^3 + \frac{1}{5}a^2 - \frac{2}{7}a\right)$

7. $\left(\frac{2}{3}x^2 - \frac{3}{4}x - 2\right) \cdot \left(\frac{4}{5}x - \frac{1}{6}x^2 - \frac{1}{2}\right)$

8. $\left(\frac{1}{6} + \frac{1}{3}x + \frac{1}{6}x^4 - \frac{1}{2}x^2\right) \cdot \left(\frac{1}{6}x^3 - \frac{1}{3} - \frac{1}{3}x\right)$

6-2 Study Guide and Intervention

Dividing Polynomials

Long Division To divide a polynomial by a monomial, use the skills learned in Lesson 6-1.

To divide a polynomial by a polynomial, use a long division pattern. Remember that only like terms can be added or subtracted.

Example 1 Simplify $\dfrac{12p^3t^2r - 21p^2qtr^2 - 9p^3tr}{3p^2tr}$.

$$\frac{12p^3t^2r - 21p^2qtr^2 - 9p^3tr}{3p^2tr} = \frac{12p^3t^2r}{3p^2tr} - \frac{21p^2qtr^2}{3p^2tr} - \frac{9p^3tr}{3p^2tr}$$

$$= \frac{12}{3}p^{(3-2)}t^{(2-1)}r^{(1-1)} - \frac{21}{3}p^{(2-2)}qt^{(1-1)}r^{(2-1)} - \frac{9}{3}p^{(3-2)}t^{(1-1)}r^{(1-1)}$$

$$= 4pt - 7qr - 3p$$

Example 2 Use long division to find $(x^3 - 8x^2 + 4x - 9) \div (x - 4)$.

$$
\begin{array}{r}
x^2 - 4x - 12 \\
x - 4 \overline{)x^3 - 8x^2 + 4x - 9} \\
\underline{(-)x^3 - 4x^2} \\
-4x^2 + 4x \\
\underline{(-)-4x^2 + 16x} \\
-12x - 9 \\
\underline{(-)-12x + 48} \\
-57
\end{array}
$$

The quotient is $x^2 - 4x - 12$, and the remainder is -57.

Therefore $\dfrac{x^3 - 8x^2 - 4x - 9}{x - 4} = x^2 - 4x - 12 - \dfrac{57}{x - 4}$.

Exercises

Simplify.

1. $\dfrac{18a^3 + 30a^2}{3a}$

2. $\dfrac{24mn^6 - 40m^2n^3}{4m^2n^3}$

3. $\dfrac{60a^2b^3 - 48b^4 + 84a^5b^2}{12ab^2}$

4. $(2x^2 - 5x - 3) \div (x - 3)$

5. $(m^2 - 3m - 7) \div (m + 2)$

6. $(p^3 - 6) \div (p - 1)$

7. $(t^3 - 6t^2 + 1) \div (t + 2)$

8. $(x^5 - 1) \div (x - 1)$

9. $(2x^3 - 5x^2 + 4x - 4) \div (x - 2)$

Lesson 6-2

6-2 Study Guide and Intervention *(continued)*
Dividing Polynomials

Synthetic Division

Synthetic division	a procedure to divide a polynomial by a binomial using coefficients of the dividend and the value of r in the divisor $x - r$

Use synthetic division to find $(2x^3 - 5x^2 + 5x - 2) \div (x - 1)$.

Step 1	Write the terms of the dividend so that the degrees of the terms are in descending order. Then write just the coefficients.	$2x^3 - 5x^2 + 5x - 2$ 2 −5 5 −2
Step 2	Write the constant r of the divisor $x - r$ to the left, In this case, $r = 1$. Bring down the first coefficient, 2, as shown.	1⌋ 2 −5 5 −2 ———————————— 2
Step 3	Multiply the first coefficient by r, $1 \cdot 2 = 2$. Write their product under the second coefficient. Then add the product and the second coefficient: $-5 + 2 = -3$.	1⌋ 2 −5 5 −2 2 ———————————— 2 −3
Step 4	Multiply the sum, −3, by r: $-3 \cdot 1 = -3$. Write the product under the next coefficient and add: $5 + (-3) = 2$.	1⌋ 2 −5 5 −2 2 −3 ———————————— 2 −3 2
Step 5	Multiply the sum, 2, by r: $2 \cdot 1 = 2$. Write the product under the next coefficient and add: $-2 + 2 = 0$. The remainder is 0.	1⌋ 2 −5 5 −2 2 −3 2 ———————————— 2 −3 2 0

Thus, $(2x^3 - 5x^2 + 5x - 2) \div (x - 1) = 2x^2 - 3x + 2$.

Exercises

Simplify.

1. $(3x^3 - 7x^2 + 9x - 14) \div (x - 2)$

2. $(5x^3 + 7x^2 - x - 3) \div (x + 1)$

3. $(2x^3 + 3x^2 - 10x - 3) \div (x + 3)$

4. $(x^3 - 8x^2 + 19x - 9) \div (x - 4)$

5. $(2x^3 + 10x^2 + 9x + 38) \div (x + 5)$

6. $(3x^3 - 8x^2 + 16x - 1) \div (x - 1)$

7. $(x^3 - 9x^2 + 17x - 1) \div (x - 2)$

8. $(4x^3 - 25x^2 + 4x + 20) \div (x - 6)$

9. $(6x^3 + 28x^2 - 7x + 9) \div (x + 5)$

10. $(x^4 - 4x^3 + x^2 + 7x - 2) \div (x - 2)$

11. $(12x^4 + 20x^3 - 24x^2 + 20x + 35) \div (3x + 5)$

6-2 Skills Practice

Dividing Polynomials

Simplify.

1. $\dfrac{10c + 6}{2}$

2. $\dfrac{12x + 20}{4}$

3. $\dfrac{15y^3 + 6y^2 + 3y}{3y}$

4. $\dfrac{12x^2 - 4x - 8}{4x}$

5. $(15q^6 + 5q^2)(5q^4)^{-1}$

6. $(4f^5 - 6f^4 + 12f^3 - 8f^2)(4f^2)^{-1}$

7. $(6j^2k - 9jk^2) \div 3jk$

8. $(4a^2h^2 - 8a^3h + 3a^4) \div (2a^2)$

9. $(n^2 + 7n + 10) \div (n + 5)$

10. $(d^2 + 4d + 3) \div (d + 1)$

11. $(2t^2 + 13t + 15) \div (t + 5)$

12. $(6y^2 + y - 2)(2y - 1)^{-1}$

13. $(4g^2 - 9) \div (2g + 3)$

14. $(2x^2 - 5x - 4) \div (x - 3)$

15. $\dfrac{u^2 + 5u - 12}{u - 3}$

16. $\dfrac{2x^2 - 5x - 4}{x - 3}$

17. $(3v^2 - 7v - 10)(v - 4)^{-1}$

18. $(3t^4 + 4t^3 - 32t^2 - 5t - 20)(t + 4)^{-1}$

19. $\dfrac{y^3 - y^2 - 6}{y + 2}$

20. $\dfrac{2x^3 - x^2 - 19x + 15}{x - 3}$

21. $(4p^3 - 3p^2 + 2p) \div (p - 1)$

22. $(3c^4 + 6c^3 - 2c + 4)(c + 2)^{-1}$

23. **GEOMETRY** The area of a rectangle is $x^3 + 8x^2 + 13x - 12$ square units. The width of the rectangle is $x + 4$ units. What is the length of the rectangle?

Lesson 6-2

6-2 Practice

Dividing Polynomials

Simplify.

1. $\dfrac{15r^{10} - 5r^8 + 40r^2}{5r^4}$

2. $\dfrac{6k^2m - 12k^3m^2 + 9m^3}{2km^2}$

3. $(-30x^3y + 12x^2y^2 - 18x^2y) \div (-6x^2y)$

4. $(-6w^3z^4 - 3w^2z^5 + 4w + 5z) \div (2w^2z)$

5. $(4a^3 - 8a^2 + a^2)(4a)^{-1}$

6. $(28d^3k^2 + d^2k^2 - 4dk^2)(4dk^2)^{-1}$

7. $\dfrac{f^2 + 7f + 10}{f + 2}$

8. $\dfrac{2x^3 + 3x - 14}{x - 2}$

9. $(a^3 - 64) \div (a - 4)$

10. $(b^3 + 27) \div (b + 3)$

11. $\dfrac{2x^3 + 6x + 152}{x + 4}$

12. $\dfrac{2x^3 + 4x - 6}{x + 3}$

13. $(3w^3 + 7w^2 - 4w + 3) \div (w + 3)$

14. $(6y^4 + 15y^3 - 28y - 6) \div (y + 2)$

15. $(x^4 - 3x^3 - 11x^2 + 3x + 10) \div (x - 5)$

16. $(3m^5 + m - 1) \div (m + 1)$

17. $(x^4 - 3x^3 + 5x - 6)(x + 2)^{-1}$

18. $(6y^2 - 5y - 15)(2y + 3)^{-1}$

19. $\dfrac{4x^2 - 2x + 6}{2x - 3}$

20. $\dfrac{6x^2 - x - 7}{3x + 1}$

21. $(2r^3 + 5r^2 - 2r - 15) \div (2r - 3)$

22. $(6t^3 + 5t^2 - 2t + 1) \div (3t + 1)$

23. $\dfrac{4p^4 - 17p^2 + 14p - 3}{2p - 3}$

24. $\dfrac{2h^4 - h^3 + h^2 + h - 3}{h^2 - 1}$

25. **GEOMETRY** The area of a rectangle is $2x^2 - 11x + 15$ square feet. The length of the rectangle is $2x - 5$ feet. What is the width of the rectangle?

26. **GEOMETRY** The area of a triangle is $15x^4 + 3x^3 + 4x^2 - x - 3$ square meters. The length of the base of the triangle is $6x^2 - 2$ meters. What is the height of the triangle?

6-2 Word Problem Practice

Dividing Polynomials

1. REMAINDERS Jordan divided the polynomial $x^4 + x - 6$ into the polynomial $p(x)$ yesterday. Today his work is smudged and he cannot read $p(x)$ or most of his answer. The only part he could read was the remainder $x + 4$. His teacher wants him to find $p(-3)$. What is $p(-3)$?

2. LONG DIVISION Dana used long division to divide $x^4 + x^3 + x^2 + x + 1$ by $x + 2$. Her work is shown below with three numbers missing.

$$
\begin{array}{r}
x^3 - x^2 + 3x - 5 \\
x + 2 \overline{)x^4 + x^3 + x^2 + x + 1} \\
(-)x^4 + 2x^3 \\
\hline
-x^3 + A \\
(-)-x^3 + 2x^2 \\
\hline
3x^2 + x \\
(-)3x^2 + B \\
\hline
-5x + 1 \\
(-)-5x - 10 \\
\hline
C
\end{array}
$$

What are A, B, and C?

3. AVERAGES Shelby is a statistician. She has a list of $n + 1$ numbers and she needs to find their average. Two of the numbers are n^3 and 2. Each of the other $n - 1$ numbers are all equal to 1. What is the average of these numbers?

4. VOLUME The volume of one column of the Lincoln Memorial is $\pi(x^3 - 32x^2 - 224x + 640)$. If the height of the column is $x + 40$ feet, find the area of the base of the column in terms of x and π.

5. NUMBER THEORY Mr. Collins has his class working with bases and polynomials. He wrote on the board that the number 1111 in base B has the value $B^3 + B^2 + B + 1$. The class was then given the following questions to answer.

a. The number 11 in base B has the value $B + 1$. What is 1111 (in base B) divided by 11 (in base B)?

b. The number 111 in base B has the value $B^2 + B + 1$. What is 1111 (in base B) divided by 111 (in base B)?

Lesson 6-2

6-2 Enrichment

Oblique Asymptotes

The graph of $y = ax + b$, where $a \neq 0$, is called an oblique asymptote of $y = f(x)$ if the graph of f comes closer and closer to the line as $x \to \infty$ or $x \to -\infty$. ∞ is the mathematical symbol for **infinity**, which means *endless*.

For $f(x) = 3x + 4 + \dfrac{2}{3}$, $y = 3x + 4$ is an oblique asymptote because

$f(x) - 3x - 4 = \dfrac{2}{x}$, and $\dfrac{2}{x} \to 0$ as $x \to \infty$ or $-\infty$. In other words, as $|x|$

increases, the value of $\dfrac{2}{x}$ gets smaller and smaller approaching 0.

Example Find the oblique asymptote for $f(x) = \dfrac{x^2 + 8x + 15}{x + 2}$.

$$\begin{array}{r|rrr}
-2 & 1 & 8 & 15 \\
   &   & -2 & -12 \\
\hline
   & 1 & 6 & \;3
\end{array}$$ Use synthetic division.

$y = \dfrac{x^2 - 8x + 15}{x + 2} = x + 6 + \dfrac{3}{x + 2}$

As $|x|$ increases, the value of $\dfrac{3}{x + 2}$ gets smaller. In other words, since

$\dfrac{3}{x + 2} \to 0$ as $x \to \infty$ or $x \to -\infty$, $y = x + 6$ is an oblique asymptote.

Exercises

Use synthetic division to find the oblique asymptote for each function.

1. $y = \dfrac{8x^2 - 4x + 11}{x + 5}$

2. $y = \dfrac{x^2 + 3x - 15}{x - 2}$

3. $y = \dfrac{x^2 - 2x - 18}{x - 3}$

4. $y = \dfrac{ax^2 + bx + c}{x - d}$

5. $y = \dfrac{ax^2 + bx + c}{x + d}$

6-3 Study Guide and Intervention
Polynomial Functions

Polynomial Functions

Polynomial in One Variable	A polynomial of degree n in one variable x is an expression of the form $a_n x^n + a_{n-1} x^{n-1} + \ldots + a_2 x^2 + a_1 x + a_0$, where the coefficients a_{n-1}, a_{n-2}, a_{n-3}, ..., a_0 represent real numbers, a_n is not zero, and n represents a nonnegative integer.

The **degree of a polynomial** in one variable is the greatest exponent of its variable. The **leading coefficient** is the coefficient of the term with the highest degree.

Polynomial Function	A polynomial function of degree n can be described by an equation of the form $P(x) = a_n x^n + a_{n-1} x^{n-1} + \ldots + a_2 x^2 + a_1 x + a_0$, where the coefficients a_{n-1}, a_{n-2}, a_{n-3}, ..., a_0 represent real numbers, a_n is not zero, and n represents a nonnegative integer.

Example 1 What are the degree and leading coefficient of $3x^2 - 2x^4 - 7 + x^3$?

Rewrite the expression so the powers of x are in decreasing order.
$-2x^4 + x^3 + 3x^2 - 7$
This is a polynomial in one variable. The degree is 4, and the leading coefficient is -2.

Example 2 Find $f(-5)$ if $f(x) = x^3 + 2x^2 - 10x + 20$.

$f(x) = x^3 + 2x^2 - 10x + 20$ Original function
$f(-5) = (-5)^3 + 2(-5)^2 - 10(-5) + 20$ Replace x with −5.
$\quad = -125 + 50 + 50 + 20$ Evaluate.
$\quad = -5$ Simplify.

Example 3 Find $g(a^2 - 1)$ if $g(x) = x^2 + 3x - 4$.

$g(x) = x^2 + 3x - 4$ Original function
$g(a^2 - 1) = (a^2 - 1)^2 + 3(a^2 - 1) - 4$ Replace x with a² − 1.
$\quad = a^4 - 2a^2 + 1 + 3a^2 - 3 - 4$ Evaluate.
$\quad = a^4 + a^2 - 6$ Simplify.

Exercises

State the degree and leading coefficient of each polynomial in one variable. If it is not a polynomial in one variable, explain why.

1. $3x^4 + 6x^3 - x^2 + 12$

2. $100 - 5x^3 + 10x^7$

3. $4x^6 + 6x^4 + 8x^8 - 10x^2 + 20$

4. $4x^2 - 3xy + 16y^2$

5. $8x^3 - 9x^5 + 4x^2 - 36$

6. $\dfrac{x^2}{18} - \dfrac{x^6}{25} + \dfrac{x^3}{36} - \dfrac{1}{72}$

Find $f(2)$ and $f(-5)$ for each function.

7. $f(x) = x^2 - 9$

8. $f(x) = 4x^3 - 3x^2 + 2x - 1$

9. $f(x) = 9x^3 - 4x^2 + 5x + 7$

Lesson 6-3

6-3 Study Guide and Intervention *(continued)*

Polynomial Functions

Graphs of Polynomial Functions

End Behavior of Polynomial Functions	If the degree is even and the leading coefficient is positive, then $f(x) \to +\infty$ as $x \to -\infty$ $\qquad f(x) \to +\infty$ as $x \to +\infty$. If the degree is even and the leading coefficient is negative, then $f(x) \to -\infty$ as $x \to -\infty$ $\qquad f(x) \to -\infty$ as $x \to +\infty$ If the degree is odd and the leading coefficient is positive, then $f(x) \to -\infty$ as $x \to -\infty$ $\qquad f(x) \to +\infty$ as $x \to +\infty$ If the degree is odd and the leading coefficient is negative, then $f(x) \to +\infty$ as $x \to -\infty$ $\qquad f(x) \to -\infty$ as $x \to +\infty$
Real Zeros of a Polynomial Function	The maximum number of zeros of a polynomial function is equal to the degree of the polynomial. A zero of a function is a point at which the graph intersects the x-axis. On a graph, count the number of real zeros of the function by counting the number of times the graph crosses or touches the x-axis.

Example   Determine whether the graph represents an odd-degree polynomial or an even-degree polynomial. Then state the number of real zeros.

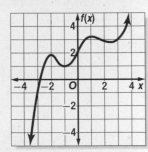

As $x \to -\infty$, $f(x) \to -\infty$ and as $x \to +\infty$, $f(x) \to +\infty$, so it is an odd-degree polynomial function.
The graph intersects the x-axis at 1 point, so the function has 1 real zero.

Exercises

For each graph,
a. describe the end behavior,
b. determine whether it represents an odd-degree or an even-degree function, and
c. state the number of real zeroes.

1.

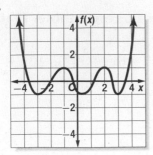

2.

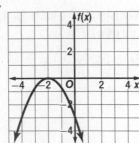

3.

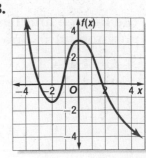

6-3 Skills Practice

Polynomial Functions

State the degree and leading coefficient of each polynomial in one variable. If it is not a polynomial in one variable, explain why.

1. $a + 8$

2. $(2x - 1)(4x^2 + 3)$

3. $-5x^5 + 3x^3 - 8$

4. $18 - 3y + 5y^2 - y^5 + 7y^6$

5. $u^3 + 4u^2t^2 + t^4$

6. $2r - r^2 + \dfrac{1}{r^2}$

Find $p(-1)$ and $p(2)$ for each function.

7. $p(x) = 4 - 3x$

8. $p(x) = 3x + x^2$

9. $p(x) = 2x^2 - 4x + 1$

10. $p(x) = -2x^3 + 5x + 3$

11. $p(x) = x^4 + 8x^2 - 10$

12. $p(x) = \dfrac{1}{3}x^2 - \dfrac{2}{3}x + 2$

If $p(x) = 4x^2 - 3$ and $r(x) = 1 + 3x$, find each value.

13. $p(a)$

14. $r(2a)$

15. $3r(a)$

16. $-4p(a)$

17. $p(a^2)$

18. $r(x + 2)$

For each graph,
a. describe the end behavior,
b. determine whether it represents an odd-degree or an even-degree function, and
c. state the number of real zeroes.

19.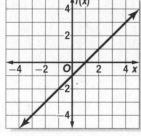

20.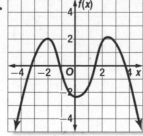

21.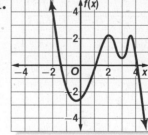

Lesson 6-3

6-3 Practice

Polynomial Functions

State the degree and leading coefficient of each polynomial in one variable. If it is not a polynomial in one variable, explain why.

1. $(3x^2 + 1)(2x^2 - 9)$

2. $\frac{1}{5}a^3 - \frac{3}{5}a^2 + \frac{4}{5}a$

3. $\frac{2}{m^2} + 3m - 12$

4. $27 + 3xy^3 - 12x^2y^2 - 10y$

Find $p(-2)$ and $p(3)$ for each function.

5. $p(x) = x^3 - x^5$

6. $p(x) = -7x^2 + 5x + 9$

7. $p(x) = -x^5 + 4x^3$

8. $p(x) = 3x^3 - x^2 + 2x - 5$

9. $p(x) = x^4 + \frac{1}{2}x^3 - \frac{1}{2}x$

10. $p(x) = \frac{1}{3x^3} + \frac{2}{3x^2} + 3x$

If $p(x) = 3x^2 - 4$ and $r(x) = 2x^2 - 5x + 1$, find each value.

11. $p(8a)$

12. $r(a^2)$

13. $-5r(2a)$

14. $r(x + 2)$

15. $p(x^2 - 1)$

16. $5p(x + 2)]$

For each graph,
a. describe the end behavior,
b. determine whether it represents an odd-degree or an even-degree function, and
c. state the number of real zeroes.

17.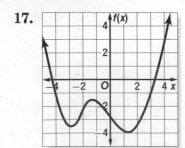

18.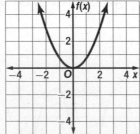

19.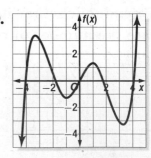

20. WIND CHILL The function $C(w) = 0.013w^2 - w - 7$ estimates the wind chill temperature $C(w)$ at 0°F for wind speeds w from 5 to 30 miles per hour. Estimate the wind chill temperature at 0°F if the wind speed is 20 miles per hour.

6-3 **Word Problem Practice**

Polynomial Functions

1. MANUFACTURING A metal sheet is curved according to the shape of the graph of $f(x) = x^4 - 9x^2$. What is the degree of this polynomial?

2. GRAPHS Kendra graphed the polynomial $f(x)$ shown below.

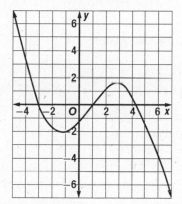

From this graph, describe the end behavior, degree, and sign of the leading coefficient.

3. PENTAGONAL NUMBERS The nth pentagonal number is given by the expression

$$\frac{n(3n - 1)}{2}.$$

What is the degree of this polynomial? What is the seventh pentagonal number?

4. DRILLING The volume of a drill bit can be estimated by the formula for a cone, $V = \frac{1}{3}\pi h r^2$, where h is the height of the bit and r is its radius. Substituting $\frac{\sqrt{3}}{3}r$ for h, the volume of the drill bit is estimated as $\frac{\sqrt{3}}{9}\pi r^3$. Graph the function of drill bit volume. Describe the end behavior, degree, and sign of the leading coefficient.

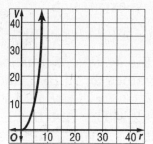

5. TRIANGLES Dylan drew n dots on a piece of paper making sure that no line contained 3 of the dots. The number of triangles that can be made using the dots as vertices is equal to $f(n) = \frac{1}{6}(n^3 - 3n^2 + 2n)$.

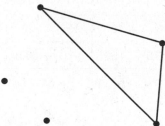

a. What is the degree of f?

b. If Dylan drew 15 dots, how many triangles can be made?

Lesson 6-3

6-3 Enrichment

Approximation by Means of Polynomials

Many scientific experiments produce pairs of numbers $[x, f(x)]$ that can be related by a formula. If the pairs form a function, you can fit a polynomial to the pairs in exactly one way. Consider the pairs given by the following table.

x	1	2	4	7
f(x)	6	11	39	−54

We will assume the polynomial is of degree three. Substitute the given values into this expression.

$$f(x) = A + B(x - x_0) + C(x - x_0)(x - x_1) + D(x - x_0)(x - x_1)(x - x_2)$$

You will get the system of equations shown below. You can solve this system and use the values for A, B, C, and D to find the desired polynomial.

$$6 = A$$
$$11 = A + B(2 - 1) = A + B$$
$$39 = A + B(4 - 1) + C(4 - 1)(4 - 2) = A + 3B + 6C$$
$$-54 = A + B(7 - 1) + C(7 - 1)(7 - 2) + D(7 - 1)(7 - 2)(7 - 4) = A + 6B + 30C + 90D$$

Solve.

1. Solve the system of equations for the values A, B, C, and D.

2. Find the polynomial that represents the four ordered pairs. Write your answer in the form $y = a + bx + cx^2 + dx^3$.

3. Find the polynomial that gives the following values.

x	8	12	15	20
f(x)	−207	169	976	3801

4. A scientist measured the volume $f(x)$ of carbon dioxide gas that can be absorbed by one cubic centimeter of charcoal at pressure x. Find the values for A, B, C, and D.

x	120	340	534	698
f(x)	3.1	5.5	7.1	8.3

6-4 Study Guide and Intervention

Analyzing Graphs of Polynomial Functions

Graphs of Polynomial Functions

Location Principle	Suppose $y = f(x)$ represents a polynomial function and a and b are two numbers such that $f(a) < 0$ and $f(b) > 0$. Then the function has at least one real zero between a and b.

Example Determine consecutive integer values of x between which each real zero of $f(x) = 2x^4 - x^3 - 5$ is located. Then draw the graph.

Make a table of values. Look at the values of $f(x)$ to locate the zeros. Then use the points to sketch a graph of the function.

x	$f(x)$
-2	35
-1	-2
0	-5
1	-4
2	19

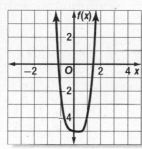

The changes in sign indicate that there are zeros between $x = -2$ and $x = -1$ and between $x = 1$ and $x = 2$.

Exercises

Graph each function by making a table of values. Determine the values of x between which each real zero is located.

1. $f(x) = x^3 - 2x^2 + 1$

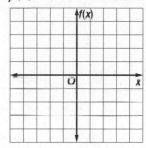

2. $f(x) = x^4 + 2x^3 - 5$

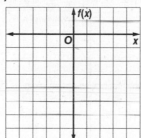

3. $f(x) = -x^4 + 2x^2 - 1$

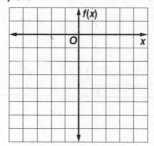

4. $f(x) = x^3 - 3x^2 + 4$

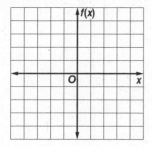

5. $f(x) = 3x^3 + 2x - 1$

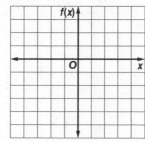

6. $f(x) = x^4 - 3x^3 + 1$

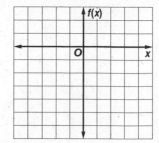

Lesson 6-4

6-4 **Study Guide and Intervention** *(continued)*

Analyzing Graphs of Polynomial Functions

Maximum and Minimum Points A quadratic function has either a maximum or a minimum point on its graph. For higher degree polynomial functions, you can find *turning points*, which represent **relative maximum** or **relative minimum** points.

Example Graph $f(x) = x^3 + 6x^2 - 3$. **Estimate the x-coordinates at which the relative maxima and minima occur.**

Make a table of values and graph the function.

x	$f(x)$	
-5	22	
-4	29	$\leftarrow$ indicates a relative maximum
-3	24	
-2	13	
-1	2	$\leftarrow$ zero between $x = -1$, $x = 0$
0	-3	$\leftarrow$ indicates a relative minimum
1	4	
2	29	

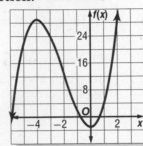

A relative maximum occurs at $x = -4$ and a relative minimum occurs at $x = 0$.

Exercises

Graph each polynomial function. Estimate the x-coordinates at which the relative maxima and relative minima occur.

1. $f(x) = x^3 - 3x^2$

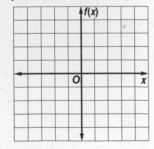

2. $f(x) = 2x^3 + x^2 - 3x$

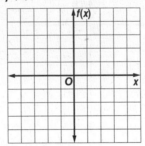

3. $f(x) = 2x^3 - 3x + 2$

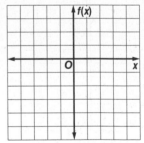

4. $f(x) = x^4 - 7x - 3$

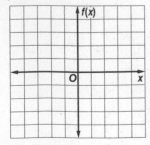

5. $f(x) = x^5 - 2x^2 + 2$

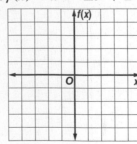

6. $f(x) = x^3 + 2x^2 - 3$

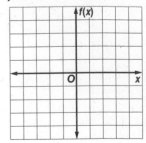

6-4 Skills Practice

Analyzing Graphs of Polynomial Functions

Complete each of the following.
a. Graph each function by making a table of values.
b. Determine the consecutive values of x between which each real zero is located.
c. Estimate the x-coordinates at which the relative maxima and minima occur.

1. $f(x) = x^3 - 3x^2 + 1$

x	f(x)
−2	
−1	
0	
1	
2	
3	
4	

2. $f(x) = x^3 - 3x + 1$

x	f(x)
−3	
−2	
−1	
0	
1	
2	
3	

3. $f(x) = 2x^3 + 9x^2 + 12x + 2$

x	f(x)
−3	
−2	
−1	
0	
1	

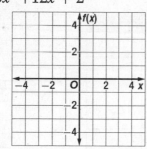

4. $f(x) = 2x^3 - 3x^2 + 2$

x	f(x)
−1	
0	
1	
2	
3	

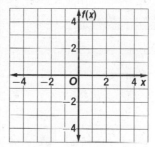

5. $f(x) = x^4 - 2x^2 - 2$

x	f(x)
−3	
−2	
−1	
0	
1	
2	
3	

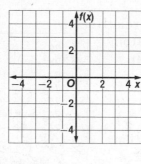

6. $f(x) = 0.5x^4 - 4x^2 + 4$

x	f(x)
−3	
−2	
−1	
0	
1	
2	
3	

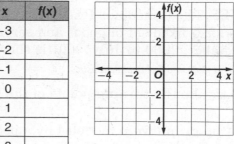

Lesson 6-4

6-4 Practice

Analyzing Graphs of Polynomial Functions

Complete each of the following.
a. Graph each function by making a table of values.
b. Determine the consecutive values of x between which each real zero is located.
c. Estimate the x-coordinates at which the relative maxima and minima occur.

1. $f(x) = -x^3 + 3x^2 - 3$

x	f(x)
-2	
-1	
0	
1	
2	
3	
4	

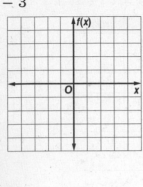

2. $f(x) = x^3 - 1.5x^2 - 6x + 1$

x	f(x)
-2	
-1	
0	
1	
2	
3	
4	

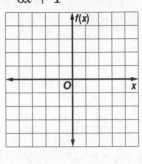

3. $f(x) = 0.75 x^4 + x^3 - 3x^2 + 4$

x	f(x)

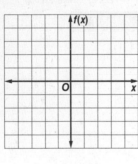

4. $f(x) = x^4 + 4x^3 + 6x^2 + 4x - 3$

x	f(x)

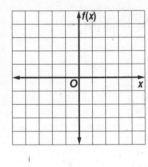

5. PRICES The Consumer Price Index (CPI) gives the relative price for a fixed set of goods and services. The CPI from September, 2000 to July, 2001 is shown in the graph.

Source: *U. S. Bureau of Labor Statistics*

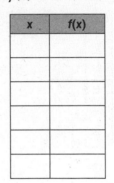

a. Describe the turning points of the graph.

b. If the graph were modeled by a polynomial equation, what is the least degree the equation could have?

6. LABOR A town's jobless rate can be modeled by (1, 3.3), (2, 4.9), (3, 5.3), (4, 6.4), (5, 4.5), (6, 5.6), (7, 2.5), and (8, 2.7). How many turning points would the graph of a polynomial function through these points have? Describe them.

6-4 Word Problem Practice

Analyzing Graphs of Polynomial Functions

1. LANDSCAPES Jalen uses a fourth-degree polynomial to describe the shape of two hills in the background of a video game that he is helping to write. The graph of the polynomial is shown below.

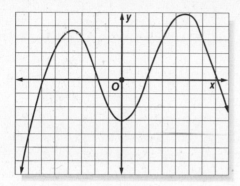

Estimate the x-coordinates at which the relative maxima and relative minima occur.

2. NATIONAL PARKS The graph models the cross-section of Mount Rushmore.

Graph Modeling Mount Rushmore

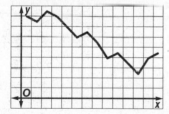

What is the smallest degree possible for the equation that corresponds with this graph?

3. VALUE A banker models the expected value of a company in millions of dollars by the formula $n^3 - 3n^2$, where n is the number of years in business. Sketch a graph of $v = n^3 - 3n^2$.

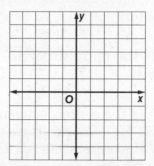

4. CONSECUTIVE NUMBERS Ms. Sanchez asks her students to write expressions to represent five consecutive integers. One solution is $x - 2$, $x - 1$, x, $x + 1$, and $x + 2$. The product of these five consecutive integers is given by the fifth degree polynomial $f(x) = x^5 - 5x^3 + 4x$.

a. For what values of x is $f(x) = 0$?

b. Sketch the graph of $y = f(x)$.

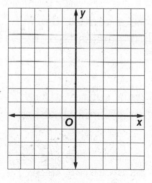

Lesson 6-4

6-4   Enrichment

Golden Rectangles

Use a straightedge, a compass, and the instructions below to construct a golden rectangle.

1. Construct square $ABCD$ with sides of 2 centimeters.

2. Construct the midpoint of $\overline{AB}$. Call the midpoint M.

3. Using M as the center, set your compass opening at MC. Construct an arc with center M that intersects $\overline{AB}$. Call the point of intersection P.

4. Construct a line through P that is perpendicular to $\overline{AB}$.

5. Extend DC so that it intersects the perpendicular. Call the intersection point Q. $APQD$ is a golden rectangle. Check this conclusion by finding the value of $\dfrac{QP}{AP}$.

A figure consisting of similar golden rectangles is shown below. Use a compass and the instructions below to draw quarter-circle arcs that form a spiral like that found in the shell of a chambered nautilus.

6. Using A as a center, draw an arc that passes through B and C.

7. Using D as a center, draw an arc that passes through C and E.

8. Using F as a center, draw an arc that passes through E and G.

9. Continue drawing arcs, using H, K, and M as the centers.

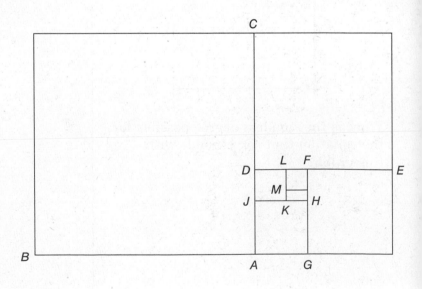

6-5 | Study Guide and Intervention

Solving Polynomial Equations

Factor Polynomials

Techniques for Factoring Polynomials	For any number of terms, check for: greatest common factor

	For two terms, check for:
	  Difference of two squares
	    $a^2 - b^2 = (a + b)(a - b)$
	  Sum of two cubes
	    $a^3 + b^3 = (a + b)(a^2 - ab + b^2)$
	  Difference of two cubes
	    $a^3 - b^3 = (a - b)(a^2 + ab + b^2)$

	For three terms, check for:
	  Perfect square trinomials
	    $a^2 + 2ab + b^2 = (a + b)^2$
	    $a^2 - 2ab + b^2 = (a - b)^2$
	  General trinomials
	    $acx^2 + (ad + bc)x + bd = (ax + b)(cx + d)$

	For four or more terms, check for:
	  Grouping
	    $ax + bx + ay + by = x(a + b) + y(a + b)$
	    $ = (a + b)(x + y)$

Example **Factor $24x^2 - 42x - 45$.**

First factor out the GCF to get $24x^2 - 42x - 45 = 3(8x^2 - 14x - 15)$. To find the coefficients of the x terms, you must find two numbers whose product is $8 \cdot (-15) = -120$ and whose sum is -14. The two coefficients must be -20 and 6. Rewrite the expression using $-20x$ and $6x$ and factor by grouping.

$8x^2 - 14x - 15 = 8x^2 - 20x + 6x - 15$ Group to find a GCF.

$ = 4x(2x - 5) + 3(2x - 5)$ Factor the GCF of each binomial.

$ = (4x + 3)(2x - 5)$ Distributive Property

Thus, $24x^2 - 42x - 45 = 3(4x + 3)(2x - 5)$.

Exercises

Factor completely. If the polynomial is not factorable, write *prime*.

1. $14x^2y^2 + 42xy^3$

2. $6mn + 18m - n - 3$

3. $2x^2 + 18x + 16$

4. $x^4 - 1$

5. $35x^3y^4 - 60x^4y$

6. $2r^3 + 250$

7. $100m^8 - 9$

8. $x^2 + x + 1$

9. $c^4 + c^3 - c^2 - c$

Lesson 6-5

6-5   Study Guide and Intervention   (continued)

Solving Polynomial Equations

Solve Polynomial Equations If a polynomial expression can be written in quadratic form, then you can use what you know about solving quadratic equations to solve the related polynomial equation.

Example 1   Solve $x^4 - 40x^2 + 144 = 0$.

$x^4 - 40x^2 + 144 = 0$	Original equation
$(x^2)^2 - 40(x^2) + 144 = 0$	Write the expression on the left in quadratic form.
$(x^2 - 4)(x^2 - 36) = 0$	Factor.

$x^2 - 4 = 0$	or $\qquad x^2 - 36 = 0$	Zero Product Property
$(x - 2)(x + 2) = 0$	or $\quad (x - 6)(x + 6) = 0$	Factor.
$x - 2 = 0$ or $x + 2 = 0$	or $x - 6 = 0$ or $x + 6 = 0$	Zero Product Property
$x = 2$ or $\qquad x = -2$	or $\qquad x = 6$ or $\qquad x = -6$	Simplify.

The solutions are ± 2 and ± 6.

Example 2   Solve $2x + \sqrt{x} - 15 = 0$.

$2x + \sqrt{x} - 15 = 0$	Original equation
$2(\sqrt{x})^2 + \sqrt{x} - 15 = 0$	Write the expression on the left in quadratic form.
$(2\sqrt{x} - 5)(\sqrt{x} + 3) = 0$	Factor.
$2\sqrt{x} - 5 = 0$ or $\sqrt{x} + 3 = 0$	Zero Product Property
$\sqrt{x} = \dfrac{5}{2}$ or $\qquad \sqrt{x} = -3$	Simplify.

Since the principal square root of a number cannot be negative, $\sqrt{x} = -3$ has no solution.
The solution is $\dfrac{25}{4}$ or $6\dfrac{1}{4}$.

Exercises

Solve each equation.

1. $x^4 = 49$

2. $x^4 - 6x^2 = -8$

3. $x^4 - 3x^2 = 54$

4. $3t^6 - 48t^2 = 0$

5. $m^6 - 16m^3 + 64 = 0$

6. $y^4 - 5y^2 + 4 = 0$

7. $x^4 - 29x^2 + 100 = 0$

8. $4x^4 - 73x^2 + 144 = 0$

9. $\dfrac{1}{x^2} - \dfrac{7}{x} + 12 = 0$

10. $x - 5\sqrt{x} + 6 = 0$

11. $x - 10\sqrt{x} + 21 = 0$

12. $x^{\frac{2}{3}} - 5x^{\frac{1}{3}} + 6 = 0$

6-5 Skills Practice

Solving Polynomial Equations

Factor completely. If the polynomial is not factorable, write *prime*.

1. $7x^2 - 14x$

2. $19x^3 - 38x^2$

3. $21x^3 - 18x^2y + 24xy^2$

4. $8j^3k - 4jk^3 - 7$

5. $a^2 + 7a - 18$

6. $2ak - 6a + k - 3$

7. $b^2 + 8b + 7$

8. $z^2 - 8z - 10$

9. $4f^2 - 64$

10. $d^2 - 12d + 36$

11. $9x^2 + 25$

12. $y^2 + 18y + 81$

13. $n^3 - 125$

14. $m^4 - 1$

Write each expression in quadratic form, if possible.

15. $5x^4 + 2x^2 - 8$

16. $3y^8 - 4y^2 + 3$

17 $100a^6 + a^3$

18. $x^8 + 4x^4 + 9$

19. $12x^4 - 7x^2$

20. $6b^5 + 3b^3 - 1$

Solve each equation.

21. $a^3 - 9a^2 + 14a = 0$

22. $x^3 = 3x^2$

23. $t^4 - 3t^3 - 40t^2 = 0$

24. $b^3 - 8b^2 + 16b = 0$

Lesson 6-5

6-5 Practice

Solving Polynomial Equations

Factor completely. If the polynomial is not factorable, write *prime*.

1. $15a^2b - 10ab^2$

2. $3st^2 - 9s^3t + 6s^2t^2$

3. $3x^3y^2 - 2x^2y + 5xy$

4. $2x^3y - x^2y + 5xy^2 + xy^3$

5. $21 - 7t + 3r - rt$

6. $x^2 - xy + 2x - 2y$

7. $y^2 + 20y + 96$

8. $4ab + 2a + 6b + 3$

9. $6n^2 - 11n - 2$

10. $6x^2 + 7x - 3$

11. $x^2 - 8x - 8$

12. $6p^2 - 17p - 45$

Write each expression in quadratic form, if possible.

13. $10b^4 + 3b^2 - 11$

14. $-5x^8 + x^2 + 6$

15. $28d^6 + 25d^3$

16. $4s^8 + 4s^4 + 7$

17. $500x^4 - x^2$

18. $8b^5 - 8b^3 - 1$

Solve each equation.

19. $y^4 - 7y^3 - 18y^2 = 0$

20. $s^5 + 4s^4 - 32s^3 = 0$

21. $m^4 - 625 = 0$

22. $n^4 - 49n^2 = 0$

23. $x^4 - 50x^2 + 49 = 0$

24. $t^4 - 21t^2 + 80 = 0$

25. PHYSICS A proton in a magnetic field follows a path on a coordinate grid modeled by the function $f(x) = x^4 - 2x^2 - 15$. What are the x-coordinates of the points on the grid where the proton crosses the x-axis?

26. SURVEYING Vista county is setting aside a large parcel of land to preserve it as open space. The county has hired Meghan's surveying firm to survey the parcel, which is in the shape of a right triangle. The longer leg of the triangle measures 5 miles less than the square of the shorter leg, and the hypotenuse of the triangle measures 13 miles less than twice the square of the shorter leg. The length of each boundary is a whole number. Find the length of each boundary.

6-5 Word Problem Practice
Solving Polynomial Equations

1. **CODES** Marisa has been trying to discover the secret code for a lock. After a long investigation, she discovers that the numbers in the secret code are solutions of the polynomial equation $x^4 - 68x^3 + 1557x^2 - 13770x + 37800 = 0$. After more work, Marisa found that $x^4 - 68x^3 + 1557x^2 - 13770x + 37800 = (x - 5)(x - 12)(x - 21)(x - 30)$. What are the numbers in the secret code?

2. **OUTPUT** Eduardo is a mechanical engineer. For one of his projects, he had to solve the polynomial equation

$$m^6 + 5m^3 - 10 = 0.$$

Write the polynomial $m^6 + 5m^3 - 10$ in quadratic form.

3. **VOLUME** A standard shipping box measures x inches high. The width is 3.5 inches more than the height, and the length is 3 inches less than the height. The volume of the box is 561 cubic inches.

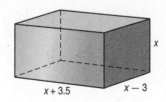

What is x?

4. **ROBOTS** A robot explorer's distance from its starting location is given by the polynomial $t^5 - 29t^3 + 100t$, where t is time measured in hours.

Factor this polynomial.

5. **PACKAGING** A small box is placed inside a larger box. The dimensions of the small box are $x + 1$ by $x + 2$ by $x - 1$. The dimensions of the larger box are $2x$ by $x + 4$ by $x + 2$.

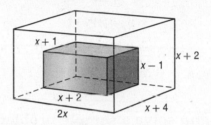

a. Write an expression for the volume of the space inside the larger box but outside the smaller box.

b. If the volume of the space inside the larger box but outside the smaller box is equal to $33x + 162$ cubic units, what is x?

c. What is the volume of the smaller box?

d. What is the volume of the larger box?

Lesson 6-5

6-5   Enrichment

History of Quadratic Equations

The ancient Babylonians are believed to be the first to solve quadratic equations, around 400 B.C. Euclid, who devised a geometrical approach in 300 B.C., followed them. Around 598–665 A.D., a Hindu mathematician named Brahmagupta created an almost modern method for solving equations. Finally, around 800 A.D., an Arab mathematician named al-Khwarizmi created a classification of quadratic equations. He classified them into six different categories and devoted a chapter to each type. His equations are made up of three different types of expressions: roots (x), squares of roots (x^2) and numbers.

For example, his first classification was squares equal to roots. A sample of this type of equations is: $x^2 = 2x$.

Now solve this quadratic equation.

$$x^2 = 2x$$

$$x^2 - 2x = 0 \qquad \text{Subtract 2x from each side.}$$

$$x(x - 2) = 0 \qquad \text{Factor.}$$

$$x = 0 \text{ or } x - 2 = 0 \qquad \text{Set both factors equal to 0.}$$

So, $x = 0$ or 2. $\qquad$ Solve.

Write and solve a sample problem for the remaining 5 classifications of quadratic equations, according to al-Khwarizmi.

1. Squares equal to numbers.

2. Roots equal to numbers.

3. Squares and roots equal to numbers.

4. Squares and numbers equal to roots.

5. Roots and numbers equal to squares.

6-6 Study Guide and Intervention

The Remainder and Factor Theorems

Synthetic Substitution

Remainder Theorem	The remainder, when you divide the polynomial $f(x)$ by $(x - a)$, is the constant $f(a)$. $f(x) = q(x) \cdot (x - a) + f(a)$, where $q(x)$ is a polynomial with degree one less than the degree of $f(x)$.

Example 1 If $f(x) = 3x^4 + 2x^3 - 5x^2 + x - 2$, find $f(-2)$.

Method 1 Synthetic Substitution

By the Remainder Theorem, $f(-2)$ should be the remainder when you divide the polynomial by $x + 2$.

$$
\begin{array}{r|rrrrr}
-2 & 3 & 2 & -5 & 1 & -2 \\
  &   & -6 & 8 & -6 & 10 \\
\hline
  & 3 & -4 & 3 & -5 & 8 \\
\end{array}
$$

The remainder is 8, so $f(-2) = 8$.

Method 2 Direct Substitution

Replace x with -2.

$$f(x) = 3x^4 + 2x^3 - 5x^2 + x - 2$$
$$f(-2) = 3(-2)^4 + 2(-2)^3 - 5(-2)^2 + (-2) - 2$$
$$= 48 - 16 - 20 - 2 - 2 \text{ or } 8$$

So $f(-2) = 8$.

Example 2 If $f(x) = 5x^3 + 2x - 1$, find $f(3)$.

Again, by the Remainder Theorem, $f(3)$ should be the remainder when you divide the polynomial by $x - 3$.

$$
\begin{array}{r|rrrr}
3 & 5 & 0 & 2 & -1 \\
  &   & 15 & 45 & 141 \\
\hline
  & 5 & 15 & 47 & 140 \\
\end{array}
$$

The remainder is 140, so $f(3) = 140$.

Exercises

Use synthetic substitution to find $f(-5)$ and $f\left(\frac{1}{2}\right)$ for each function.

1. $f(x) = -3x^2 + 5x - 1$

2. $f(x) = 4x^2 + 6x - 7$

3. $f(x) = -x^3 + 3x^2 - 5$

4. $f(x) = x^4 + 11x^2 - 1$

Use synthetic substitution to find $f(4)$ and $f(-3)$ for each function.

5. $f(x) = 2x^3 + x^2 - 5x + 3$

6. $f(x) = 3x^3 - 4x + 2$

7. $f(x) = 5x^3 - 4x^2 + 2$

8. $f(x) = 2x^4 - 4x^3 + 3x^2 + x - 6$

9. $f(x) = 5x^4 + 3x^3 - 4x^2 - 2x + 4$

10. $f(x) = 3x^4 - 2x^3 - x^2 + 2x - 5$

11. $f(x) = 2x^4 - 4x^3 - x^2 - 6x + 3$

12. $f(x) = 4x^4 - 4x^3 + 3x^2 - 2x - 3$

6-6 Study Guide and Intervention *(continued)*

The Remainder and Factor Theorems

Factors of Polynomials The **Factor Theorem** can help you find all the factors of a polynomial.

Factor Theorem	The binomial $x - a$ is a factor of the polynomial $f(x)$ if and only if $f(a) = 0$.

Example Show that $x + 5$ is a factor of $x^3 + 2x^2 - 13x + 10$. Then find the remaining factors of the polynomial.

By the Factor Theorem, the binomial $x + 5$ is a factor of the polynomial if -5 is a zero of the polynomial function. To check this, use synthetic substitution.

$$
\begin{array}{r|rrrr}
-5 & 1 & 2 & -13 & 10 \\
   &   & -5 & 15 & -10 \\
\hline
   & 1 & -3 & 2 & 0
\end{array}
$$

Since the remainder is 0, $x + 5$ is a factor of the polynomial. The polynomial $x^3 + 2x^2 - 13x + 10$ can be factored as $(x + 5)(x^2 - 3x + 2)$. The depressed polynomial $x^2 - 3x + 2$ can be factored as $(x - 2)(x - 1)$.

So $x^3 + 2x^2 - 13x + 10 = (x + 5)(x - 2)(x - 1)$.

Exercises

Given a polynomial and one of its factors, find the remaining factors of the polynomial.

1. $x^3 + x^2 - 10x + 8;\ x - 2$

2. $x^3 - 4x^2 - 11x + 30;\ x + 3$

3. $x^3 + 15x^2 + 71x + 105;\ x + 7$

4. $x^3 - 7x^2 - 26x + 72;\ x + 4$

5. $2x^3 - x^2 - 7x + 6;\ x - 1$

6. $3x^3 - x^2 - 62x - 40;\ x + 4$

7. $12x^3 - 71x^2 + 57x - 10;\ x - 5$

8. $14x^3 + x^2 - 24x + 9;\ x - 1$

9. $x^3 + x + 10;\ x + 2$

10. $2x^3 - 11x^2 + 19x - 28;\ x - 4$

11. $3x^3 - 13x^2 - 34x + 24;\ x - 6$

12. $x^4 + x^3 - 11x^2 - 9x + 18;\ x - 1$

6-6   Skills Practice

The Remainder and Factor Theorems

Use synthetic substitution to find $f(2)$ and $f(-1)$ for each function.

1. $f(x) = x^2 + 6x + 5$ **2.** $f(x) = x^2 - x + 1$

3. $f(x) = x^2 - 2x - 2$ **4.** $f(x) = x^3 + 2x^2 + 5$

5. $f(x) = x^3 - x^2 - 2x + 3$ **6.** $f(x) = x^3 + 6x^2 + x - 4$

7. $f(x) = x^3 - 3x^2 + x - 2$ **8.** $f(x) = x^3 - 5x^2 - x + 6$

9. $f(x) = x^4 + 2x^2 - 9$ **10.** $f(x) = x^4 - 3x^3 + 2x^2 - 2x + 6$

11. $f(x) = x^5 - 7x^3 - 4x + 10$ **12.** $f(x) = x^6 - 2x^5 + x^4 + x^3 - 9x^2 - 20$

Given a polynomial and one of its factors, find the remaining factors of the polynomial.

13. $x^3 + 2x^2 - x - 2; x + 1$ **14.** $x^3 + x^2 - 5x + 3; x - 1$

15. $x^3 + 3x^2 - 4x - 12; x + 3$ **16.** $x^3 - 6x^2 + 11x - 6; x - 3$

17. $x^3 + 2x^2 - 33x - 90; x + 5$ **18.** $x^3 - 6x^2 + 32; x - 4$

19. $x^3 - x^2 - 10x - 8; x + 2$ **20.** $x^3 - 19x + 30; x - 2$

21. $2x^3 + x^2 - 2x - 1; x + 1$ **22.** $2x^3 + x^2 - 5x + 2; x + 2$

23. $3x^3 + 4x^2 - 5x - 2; 3x + 1$ **24.** $3x^3 + x^2 + x - 2; 3x - 2$

6-6 Practice

The Remainder and Factor Theorems

Use synthetic substitution to find $f(-3)$ and $f(4)$ for each function.

1. $f(x) = x^2 + 2x + 3$

2. $f(x) = x^2 - 5x + 10$

3. $f(x) = x^2 - 5x - 4$

4. $f(x) = x^3 - x^2 - 2x + 3$

5. $f(x) = x^3 + 2x^2 + 5$

6. $f(x) = x^3 - 6x^2 + 2x$

7. $f(x) = x^3 - 2x^2 - 2x + 8$

8. $f(x) = x^3 - x^2 + 4x - 4$

9. $f(x) = x^3 + 3x^2 + 2x - 50$

10. $f(x) = x^4 + x^3 - 3x^2 - x + 12$

11. $f(x) = x^4 - 2x^2 - x + 7$

12. $f(x) = 2x^4 - 3x^3 + 4x^2 - 2x + 1$

13. $f(x) = 2x^4 - x^3 + 2x^2 - 26$

14. $f(x) = 3x^4 - 4x^3 + 3x^2 - 5x - 3$

15. $f(x) = x^5 + 7x^3 - 4x - 10$

16. $f(x) = x^6 + 2x^5 - x^4 + x^3 - 9x^2 + 20$

Given a polynomial and one of its factors, find the remaining factors of the polynomial.

17. $x^3 + 3x^2 - 6x - 8$; $x - 2$

18. $x^3 + 7x^2 + 7x - 15$; $x - 1$

19. $x^3 - 9x^2 + 27x - 27$; $x - 3$

20. $x^3 - x^2 - 8x + 12$; $x + 3$

21. $x^3 + 5x^2 - 2x - 24$; $x - 2$

22. $x^3 - x^2 - 14x + 24$; $x + 4$

23. $3x^3 - 4x^2 - 17x + 6$; $x + 2$

24. $4x^3 - 12x^2 - x + 3$; $x - 3$

25. $18x^3 + 9x^2 - 2x - 1$; $2x + 1$

26. $6x^3 + 5x^2 - 3x - 2$; $3x - 2$

27. $x^5 + x^4 - 5x^3 - 5x^2 + 4x + 4$; $x + 1$

28. $x^5 - 2x^4 + 4x^3 - 8x^2 - 5x + 10$; $x - 2$

29. **POPULATION** The projected population in thousands for a city over the next several years can be estimated by the function $P(x) = x^3 + 2x^2 - 8x + 520$, where x is the number of years since 2005. Use synthetic substitution to estimate the population for 2010.

30. **VOLUME** The volume of water in a rectangular swimming pool can be modeled by the polynomial $2x^3 - 9x^2 + 7x + 6$. If the depth of the pool is given by the polynomial $2x + 1$, what polynomials express the length and width of the pool?

6-6   **Word Problem Practice**

The Remainder and Factor Theorems

1. HEIGHT A ball tossed into the air follows a parabolic trajectory. Its height after t seconds is given by a polynomial of degree two with leading coefficient -16. Using synthetic substitution, Norman found that the polynomial evaluates to 0 for the values $t = 0$ and $t - 4$. What is the polynomial that describes the ball's height as a function of t?

2. SYNTHETIC SUBSTITUTION
Branford evaluates the polynomial $p(x) = x^3 - 5x^2 + 3x + 5$ for a factor using synthetic substitution. Some of his work is shown below. Unfortunately, the factor and the solution have ink spots over it.

$$
\begin{array}{r|rrrr}
\text{✹} & 1 & -5 & 3 & 5 \\
& & 11 & 66 & 759 \\
\hline
& 1 & 6 & 69 & \text{✹}
\end{array}
$$

What is the factor he solved for? What is the hidden solution?

3. PROFIT The profits of Clyde's Corporation can be modeled by the polynomial $P(y) = y^4 - 4y^3 + 2y^2 + 10y - 200$, where y is the number of years after the business was started. The chief financial officer wants to know the value of $P(10)$. Use synthetic substitution to determine $P(10)$. Show your work.

4. EXPONENTIALS The exponential function $t = e^x$ is a special function that you will learn about later. It is not a polynomial function. However, for small values of x, the value of e^x is very closely approximated by the polynomial function

$$e(x) = \frac{1}{6}x^3 + \frac{1}{2}x^2 + x + 1.$$

Use synthetic substitution to determine $e(0.1)$. Show your work.

5. VOLUME The volume in cubic feet of one popular size of above-ground pool is given by the polynomial

$$v(x) = \pi(x^3 - 5x^2 - 80x + 360).$$

a. Use synthetic division to show that $x - 4$ is a factor of $v(x)$. Show your work.

b. Factor $v(x)$ completely.

c. What is the value of $v(10)$?

6-6 Enrichment

Radical Notation

In 1494, the first Edition of *Summa de arithmetica geometrica proprtioni et proportionalita*, now known as the *Suma*, was printed in Italy. The author, Luca Pacioli, wrote the book as a summary of the mathematical knowledge at the time. However, the notation used in the book is quite similar to the notation used today. For example, to represent radicals, the following was used:

$$6 \cdot p \cdot R \cdot 10$$

In our notation, the p represents "plus" and the R represents "radical." So, $6 \cdot p \cdot R \cdot 10$ means $6 + \sqrt{10}$.

1. What letter would you expect to represent subtraction?

2. Translate the following notations into modern notation.

a. $18 \cdot m \cdot R \cdot 90$

b. $108 \cdot m \cdot R \cdot 3240 \cdot p \cdot R \cdot 3240 \cdot m \cdot R \cdot 900$

c. $10 \cdot R \cdot 5 \cdot p \cdot 2 \cdot R \cdot 3$

3. Translate the following into notations from 1494.

a. $32\sqrt{10}$

b. $21\sqrt{6} + 3\sqrt{3}$

c. $5\sqrt{2} - 2 + 7\sqrt{11}$

6-7 Study Guide and Intervention

Roots and Zeros

Synthetic Types of Roots The following statements are equivalent for any polynomial function $f(x)$.

- c is a zero of the polynomial function $f(x)$.
- c is a root or solution of the polynomial equation $f(x) = 0$.
- $(x - c)$ is a factor of the polynomial $f(x)$.
- If c is real, then $(c, 0)$ is an intercept of the graph of $f(x)$.

Fundamental Theorem of Algebra	Every polynomial equation with degree greater than zero has at least one root in the set of complex numbers.
Corollary to the Fundamental Theorem of Algebras	A polynomial equation of the form $P(x) = 0$ of degree n with complex coefficients has exactly n roots in the set of complex numbers, including repeated roots.
Descartes' Rule of Signs	If $P(x)$ is a polynomial with real coefficients whose terms are arranged in descending powers of the variable, • the number of positive real zeros of $y = P(x)$ is the same as the number of changes in sign of the coefficients of the terms, or is less than this by an even number, and • the number of negative real zeros of $y = P(x)$ is the same as the number of changes in sign of the coefficients of the terms of $P(-x)$, or is less than this number by an even number.

Example 1 Solve the equation $6x^3 + 3x = 0$. State the number and type of roots.

$6x^3 + 3x = 0$

$3x(2x^2 + 1) = 0$

Use the Zero Product Property.

$3x = 0$ or $2x^2 + 1 = 0$

$x = 0$ or $2x^2 = -1$

$x = \pm \dfrac{i\sqrt{2}}{2}$

The equation has one real root, 0,

and two imaginary roots, $\pm \dfrac{i\sqrt{2}}{2}$.

Example 2 State the number of positive real zeros, negative real zeros, and imaginary zeros for $p(x) = 4x^4 - 3x^3 - x^2 + 2x - 5$.

Since $p(x)$ has degree 4, it has 4 zeros.

Since there are three sign changes, there are 3 or 1 positive real zeros.

Find $p(-x)$ and count the number of changes in sign for its coefficients.

$p(-x) = 4(-x)^4 - 3(-x)^3 + (-x)^2 + 2(-x) - 5$

$= 4x^4 + 3x^3 + x^2 - 2x - 5$

Since there is one sign change, there is exactly 1 negative real zero.

Thus, there are 3 positive and 1 negative real zero or 1 positive and 1 negative real zeros and 2 imaginary zeros.

Exercises

Solve each equation. State the number and type of roots.

1. $x^2 + 4x - 21 = 0$

2. $2x^3 - 50x = 0$

3. $12x^3 + 100x = 0$

State the possible number of positive real zeros, negative real zeros, and imaginary zeros for each function.

4. $f(x) = 3x^3 + x^2 - 8x - 12$

5. $f(x) = 3x^5 - x^4 - x^3 + 6x^2 - 5$

6-7 Study Guide and Intervention (continued)

Roots and Zeros

Find Zeros

Complex Conjugate Theorem	Suppose a and b are real numbers with $b \neq 0$. If $a + bi$ is a zero of a polynomial function with real coefficients, then $a - bi$ is also a zero of the function.

Example Find all of the zeros of $f(x) = x^4 - 15x^2 + 38x - 60$.

Since $f(x)$ has degree 4, the function has 4 zeros.

$f(x) = x^4 - 15x^2 + 38x - 60$ $f(-x) = x^4 - 15x^2 - 38x - 60$

Since there are 3 sign changes for the coefficients of $f(x)$, the function has 3 or 1 positive real zeros. Since there is + sign change for the coefficients of $f(-x)$, the function has 1 negative real zero. Use synthetic substitution to test some possible zeros.

$$\begin{array}{r|rrrrr}
2 & 1 & 0 & -15 & 38 & -60 \\
  &   & 2 & 4 & -22 & 32 \\
\hline
  & 1 & 2 & -11 & 16 & -28 \\
\end{array}$$

$$\begin{array}{r|rrrrr}
3 & 1 & 0 & -15 & 38 & -60 \\
  &   & 3 & 9 & -18 & 60 \\
\hline
  & 1 & 3 & -6 & 20 & 0 \\
\end{array}$$

So 3 is a zero of the polynomial function. Now try synthetic substitution again to find a zero of the depressed polynomial.

$$\begin{array}{r|rrrr}
-2 & 1 & 3 & -6 & 20 \\
   &   & -2 & -2 & 16 \\
\hline
   & 1 & 1 & -8 & 36 \\
\end{array}$$

$$\begin{array}{r|rrrr}
-4 & 1 & 3 & -6 & 20 \\
   &   & -4 & 4 & 8 \\
\hline
   & 1 & -1 & -2 & 28 \\
\end{array}$$

$$\begin{array}{r|rrrr}
-5 & 1 & 3 & -6 & 20 \\
   &   & -5 & 10 & -20 \\
\hline
   & 1 & -2 & 4 & 0 \\
\end{array}$$

So -5 is another zero. Use the Quadratic Formula on the depressed polynomial $x^2 - 2x + 4$ to find the other 1 zeros, $1 \pm i\sqrt{3}$.

The function has two real zeros at 3 and -5 and two imaginary zeros at $1 \pm i\sqrt{3}$.

Exercises

Find all zeros of each function.

1. $f(x) = x^3 + x^2 + 9x + 9$

2. $f(x) = x^3 - 3x^2 + 4x - 12$

3. $p(a) = a^3 - 10a^2 + 34a - 40$

4. $p(x) = x^3 - 5x^2 + 11x - 15$

5. $f(x) = x^3 + 6x + 20$

6. $f(x) = x^4 - 3x^3 + 21x^2 - 75x - 100$

6-7 Skills Practice

Roots and Zeros

Solve each equation. State the number and type of roots.

1. $5x + 12 = 0$

2. $x^2 - 4x + 40 = 0$

3. $x^5 + 4x^3 = 0$

4. $x^4 - 625 = 0$

5. $4x^2 - 4x - 1 = 0$

6. $x^5 - 81x = 0$

State the possible number of positive real zeros, negative real zeros, and imaginary zeros of each function.

7. $g(x) = 3x^3 - 4x^2 - 17x + 6$

8. $h(x) = 4x^3 - 12x^2 - x + 3$

9. $f(x) = x^3 - 8x^2 + 2x - 4$

10. $p(x) = x^3 - x^2 + 4x - 6$

11. $q(x) = x^4 + 7x^2 + 3x - 9$

12. $f(x) = x^4 - x^3 - 5x^2 + 6x + 1$

Find all the zeros of each function.

13. $h(x) = x^3 - 5x^2 + 5x + 3$

14. $g(x) = x^3 - 6x^2 + 13x - 10$

15. $h(x) = x^3 + 4x^2 + x - 6$

16. $q(x) = x^3 + 3x^2 - 6x - 8$

17. $g(x) = x^4 - 3x^3 - 5x^2 + 3x + 4$

18. $f(x) = x^4 - 21x^2 + 80$

Write a polynomial function of least degree with integral coefficients that have the given zeros.

19. $-3, -5, 1$

20. $3i$

21. $-5 + i$

22. $-1, \sqrt{3}, -\sqrt{3}$

23. $i, 5i$

24. $-1, 1, i\sqrt{6}$

Lesson 6-7

6-7 Practice

Roots and Zeros

Solve each equation. State the number and type of roots.

1. $-9x - 15 = 0$

2. $x^4 - 5x^2 + 4 = 0$

3. $x^5 - 81x = 0$

4. $x^3 + x^2 - 3x - 3 = 0$

5. $x^3 + 6x + 20 = 0$

6. $x^4 - x^3 - x^2 - x - 2 = 0$

State the possible number of positive real zeros, negative real zeros, and imaginary zeros of each function.

7. $f(x) = 4x^3 - 2x^2 + x + 3$

8. $p(x) = 2x^4 - 2x^3 + 2x^2 - x - 1$

9. $q(x) = 3x^4 + x^3 - 3x^2 + 7x + 5$

10. $h(x) = 7x^4 + 3x^3 - 2x^2 - x + 1$

Find all zeros of each function.

11. $h(x) = 2x^3 + 3x^2 - 65x + 84$

12. $p(x) = x^3 - 3x^2 + 9x - 7$

13. $h(x) = x^3 - 7x^2 + 17x - +5$

14. $q(x) = x^4 + 50x^2 + 49$

15. $g(x) = x^4 + 4x^3 - 3x^2 - 14x - 8$

16. $f(x) = x^4 - 6x^3 + 6x^2 + 24x - 40$

Write a polynomial function of least degree with integral coefficients that has the given zeros.

17. $-5, 3i$

18. $-2, 3 + i$

19. $-1, 4, 3i$

20. $2, 5, 1 + i$

21. **CRAFTS** Stephan has a set of plans to build a wooden box. He wants to reduce the volume of the box to 105 cubic inches. He would like to reduce the length of each dimension in the plan by the same amount. The plans call for the box to be 10 inches by 8 inches by 6 inches. Write and solve a polynomial equation to find out how much Stephan should take from each dimension.

6-7 Word Problem Practice

Roots and Zeros

1. TABLES Li Pang made a table of values for the polynomial $p(x)$. Her table is shown below.

x	p(x)
−4	−3
−3	−1
−2	0
−1	2
0	0
1	4
2	0
3	2
4	5

Name three roots of $p(x)$.

2. ROOTS Ryan is an electrical engineer. He often solves polynomial equations to work out various properties of the circuits he builds. For one circuit, he must find the roots of a polynomial $p(x)$. He finds that $p(2 - 3i) = 0$. Give two different roots of $p(x)$.

3. REAL ROOTS There are more than a thousand roller coasters around the world. Roller coaster designers can use polynomial functions to model the shapes of possible roller coasters. Madison is studying a roller coaster modeled by the polynomial $f(x) = x^6 - 14x^4 + 49x^2 - 36$. She knows that all of the roots of $f(x)$ are real. How many positive and how many negative roots are there? How are the set of positive roots and negative roots related to each other? Explain.

4. COMPLEX ROOTS Eric is a statistician. During the course of his work, he had to find something called the "eigenvalues of a matrix," which was basically the same as finding the roots of a polynomial. The polynomial was $x^4 + 6x^2 + 25$. One of the roots of this polynomial is $1 + 2i$. What are the other 3 roots? Explain.

5. QUADRILATERALS Shayna plotted the four vertices of a quadrilateral in the complex plane and then encoded the points in a polynomial $p(x)$ by making them the roots of $p(x)$. The polynomial $p(x)$ is $x^4 - 9x^3 + 27x^2 + 23x - 150$.

a. The polynomial $p(x)$ has one positive real root, and it is an integer. Find the integer.

b. Find the negative real root(s) of $p(x)$.

c. Find the complex roots of $p(x)$.

6-7   Enrichment

The Bisection Method for Approximating Real Zeros

The **bisection method** can be used to approximate zeros of polynomial functions like $f(x) = x^3 + x^2 - 3x - 3$.

Since $f(1) = -4$ and $f(2) = 3$, there is at least one real zero between 1 and 2. The midpoint of this interval $\dfrac{1+2}{2} = 1.5$. Since $f(1.5) = -1.875$, the zero is between 1.5 and 2. The midpoint of this interval is $\dfrac{1.5+2}{2} = 1.75$. Since $f(1.75)$ is about 0.172, the zero is between 1.5 and 1.75. The midpoint of this interval is $\dfrac{1.5+1.75}{2} = 1.625$ and $f(1.625)$ is about -0.94. The zero is between 1.625 and 1.75. The midpoint of this interval is $\dfrac{1.625+1.75}{2} = 1.6875$. Since $f(1.6875)$ is about -0.41, the zero is between 1.6875 and 1.75. Therefore, the zero is 1.7 to the nearest tenth.

The diagram below summarizes the results obtained by the bisection method.

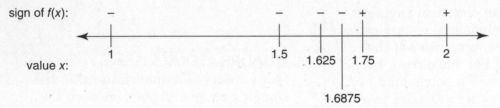

Using the bisection method, approximate to the nearest tenth the zero between the two integral values of x for each function.

1. $f(x) = x^3 - 4x^2 - 11x + 2,\ f(0) = 2,\ f(1) = -12$

2. $f(x) = 2x^4 + x^2 - 15,\ f(1) = -12,\ f(2) = 21$

3. $f(x) = x^5 - 2x^3 - 12,\ f(1) = -13,\ f(2) = 4$

4. $f(x) = 4x^3 - 2x + 7,\ f(-2) = -21,\ f(-1) = 5$

5. $f(x) = 3x^3 - 14x^2 - 27x + 126,\ f(4) = -14,\ f(5) = 16$

6-8 Study Guide and Intervention
Rational Zero Theorem

Identify Rational Zeros

Rational Zero Theorem	Let $f(x) = a_n x^n + a_{n-1} x^{n-1} + \ldots + a_2 x^2 + a_1 x + a_0$ represent a polynomial function with integral coefficients. If $\frac{p}{q}$ is a rational number in simplest form and is a zero of $y = f(x)$, then p is a factor of a_0 and q is a factor of a_n.
Corollary (Integral Zero Theorem)	If the coefficients of a polynomial are integers such that $a_n = 1$ and $a_0 \neq 0$, any rational zeros of the function must be factors of a_0.

Example **List all of the possible rational zeros of each function.**

a. $f(x) = 3x^4 - 2x^2 + 6x - 10$

If $\frac{p}{q}$ is a rational root, then p is a factor of -10 and q is a factor of 3. The possible values for p are ± 1, ± 2, ± 5, and ± 10. The possible values for q are 61 and 63. So all of the possible rational zeros are $\frac{p}{q} = \pm 1$, ± 2, ± 5, ± 10, $\pm \frac{1}{3}$, $\pm \frac{2}{3}$, $\pm \frac{5}{3}$, and $\pm \frac{10}{3}$.

b. $q(x) = x^3 - 10x^2 + 14x - 36$

Since the coefficient of x^3 is 1, the possible rational zeros must be the factors of the constant term -36. So the possible rational zeros are ± 1, ± 2, ± 3, ± 4, ± 6, ± 9, ± 12, ± 18, and ± 36.

Exercises

List all of the possible rational zeros of each function.

1. $f(x) = x^3 + 3x^2 - x + 8$

2. $g(x) = x^5 - 7x^4 + 3x^2 + x - 20$

3. $h(x) = x^4 - 7x^3 - 4x^2 + x - 49$

4. $p(x) = 2x^4 - 5x^3 + 8x^2 + 3x - 5$

5. $q(x) = 3x^4 - 5x^3 + 10x + 12$

6. $r(x) = 4x^5 - 2x + 18$

7. $f(x) = x^7 - 6x^5 - 3x^4 + x^3 + 4x^2 - 120$

8. $g(x) = 5x^6 - 3x^4 + 5x^3 + 2x^2 - 15$

9. $h(x) = 6x^5 - 3x^4 + 12x^3 + 18x^2 - 9x + 21$

10. $p(x) = 2x^7 - 3x^6 + 11x^5 - 20x^2 + 11$

6-8 Study Guide and Intervention *(continued)*

Rational Zero Theorem

Find Rational Zeros

Example 1 **Find all of the rational zeros of $f(x) = 5x^3 + 12x^2 - 29x + 12$.**

From the corollary to the Fundamental Theorem of Algebra, we know that there are exactly 3 complex roots. According to Descartes' Rule of Signs there are 2 or 0 positive real roots and 1 negative real root. The possible rational zeros are ± 1, ± 2, ± 3, ± 4, ± 6, ± 12, $\pm\frac{1}{5}$, $\pm\frac{2}{5}$, $\pm\frac{3}{5}$, $\pm\frac{4}{5}$, $\pm\frac{6}{5}$, $\pm\frac{12}{5}$. Make a table and test some possible rational zeros.

$\frac{p}{q}$	5	12	−29	12
1	5	17	−12	0

Since $f(1) = 0$, you know that $x = 1$ is a zero.

The depressed polynomial is $5x^2 + 17x - 12$, which can be factored as $(5x - 3)(x + 4)$.

By the Zero Product Property, this expression equals 0 when $x = \frac{3}{5}$ or $x = -4$.

The rational zeros of this function are 1, $\frac{3}{5}$, and -4.

Example 2 **Find all of the zeros of $f(x) = 8x^4 + 2x^3 + 5x^2 + 2x - 3$.**

There are 4 complex roots, with 1 positive real root and 3 or 1 negative real roots. The possible rational zeros are ± 1, ± 3, $\pm\frac{1}{2}$, $\pm\frac{1}{4}$, $\pm\frac{1}{8}$, $\pm\frac{3}{2}$, $\pm\frac{3}{4}$, and $\pm\frac{3}{8}$.

Make a table and test some possible values.

$\frac{p}{q}$	8	2	5	2	−3
1	8	10	15	17	14
2	8	18	41	84	165
$\frac{1}{2}$	8	6	8	6	0

Since $f\left(\frac{1}{2}\right) = 0$, we know that $x = \frac{1}{2}$ is a root.

The depressed polynomial is $8x^3 + 6x^2 + 8x + 6$. Try synthetic substitution again. Any remaining rational roots must be negative.

$\frac{p}{q}$	8	6	8	6
$-\frac{1}{4}$	8	4	7	$4\frac{1}{4}$
$-\frac{3}{4}$	8	0	8	0

$x = -\frac{3}{4}$ is another rational root.
The depressed polynomial is $8x^2 + 8 = 0$, which has roots $\pm i$.

The zeros of this function are $\frac{1}{2}$, $-\frac{3}{4}$, and $\pm i$.

Exercises

Find all of the rational zeros of each function.

1. $f(x) = x^3 + 4x^2 - 25x - 28$

2. $f(x) = x^3 + 6x^2 + 4x + 24$

Find all of the zeros of each function.

3. $f(x) = x^4 + 2x^3 - 11x^2 + 8x - 60$

4. $f(x) = 4x^4 + 5x^3 + 30x^2 + 45x - 54$

6-8 Skills Practice

Rational Zero Theorem

List all of the possible rational zeros of each function.

1. $n(x) = x^2 + 5x + 3$

2. $h(x) = x^2 - 2x - 5$

3. $w(x) = x^2 - 5x + 12$

4. $f(x) = 2x^2 + 5x + 3$

5. $q(x) = 6x^3 + x^2 - x + 2$

6. $g(x) = 9x^4 + 3x^3 + 3x^2 - x + 27$

Find all of the rational zeros of each function.

7. $f(x) = x^3 - 2x^2 + 5x - 4$

8. $g(x) = x^3 - 3x^2 - 4x + 12$

9. $p(x) = x^3 - x^2 + x - 1$

10. $z(x) = x^3 - 4x^2 + 6x - 4$

11. $h(x) = x^3 - x^2 + 4x - 4$

12. $g(x) = 3x^3 - 9x^2 - 10x - 8$

13. $g(x) = 2x^3 + 7x^2 - 7x - 12$

14. $h(x) = 2x^3 - 5x^2 - 4x + 3$

15. $p(x) = 3x^3 - 5x^2 - 14x - 4$

16. $q(x) = 3x^3 + 2x^2 + 27x + 18$

17. $q(x) = 3x^3 - 7x^2 + 4$

18. $f(x) = x^4 - 2x^3 - 13x^2 + 14x + 24$

19. $p(x) = x^4 - 5x^3 - 9x^2 - 25x - 70$

20. $n(x) = 16x^4 - 32x^3 - 13x^2 + 29x - 6$

Find all of the zeros of each function.

21. $f(x) = x^3 + 5x^2 + 11x + 15$

22. $q(x) = x^3 - 10x^2 + 18x - 4$

23. $m(x) = 6x^4 - 17x^3 + 8x^2 + 8x - 3$

24. $g(x) = x^4 + 4x^3 + 5x^2 + 4x + 4$

6-8 Practice

Rational Zero Theorem

List all of the possible rational zeros of each function.

1. $h(x) = x^3 - 5x^2 + 2x + 12$

2. $s(x) = x^4 - 8x^3 + 7x - 14$

3. $f(x) = 3x^5 - 5x^2 + x + 6$

4. $p(x) = 3x^2 + x + 7$

5. $g(x) = 5x^3 + x^2 - x + 8$

6. $q(x) = 6x^5 + x^3 - 3$

Find all of the rational zeros of each function.

7. $q(x) = x^3 + 3x^2 - 6x - 8$

8. $v(x) = x^3 - 9x^2 + 27x - 27$

9. $c(x) = x^3 - x^2 - 8x + 12$

10. $f(x) = x^4 - 49x^2$

11. $h(x) = x^3 - 7x^2 + 17x - 15$

12. $b(x) = x^3 + 6x + 20$

13. $f(x) = x^3 - 6x^2 + 4x - 24$

14. $g(x) = 2x^3 + 3x^2 - 4x - 4$

15. $h(x) = 2x^3 - 7x^2 - 21x + 54$

16. $z(x) = x^4 - 3x^3 + 5x^2 - 27x - 36$

17. $d(x) = x^4 + x^3 + 16$

18. $n(x) = x^4 - 2x^3 - 3$

19. $p(x) = 2x^4 - 7x^3 + 4x^2 + 7x - 6$

20. $q(x) = 6x^4 + -9x^3 + 40x^2 + 7x - 12$

Find all of the zeros of each function.

21. $f(x) = 2x^4 + 7x^3 - 2x^2 - 19x - 12$

22. $q(x) = x^4 - 4x^3 + x^2 + 16x - 20$

23. $h(x) = x^6 - 8x^3$

24. $g(x) = x^6 - 1$

25. **TRAVEL** The height of a box that Joan is shipping is 3 inches less than the width of the box. The length is 2 inches more than twice the width. The volume of the box is 1540 in³. What are the dimensions of the box?

26. **GEOMETRY** The height of a square pyramid is 3 meters shorter than the side of its base. If the volume of the pyramid is 432 m³, how tall is it? Use the formula $V = \frac{1}{3}Bh$.

6-8 Word Problem Practice

Rational Zero Theorem

1. ROOTS Paul was examining an old algebra book. He came upon a page about polynomial equations and saw the polynomial below.

As you can see, all the middle terms were blotted out by an ink spill. What are all the possible rational roots of this polynomial?

2. IRRATIONAL CONSTANTS Cherie was given a polynomial whose constant term was $\sqrt{2}$. Is it possible for this polynomial to have a rational root? If it is not, explain why not. If it is possible, give an example of such a polynomial with a rational root.

3. MARKOV CHAINS Tara is a mathematician who specializes in probability. In the course of her work, she needed to find the roots of the polynomial
$p(x) = 288x^4 - 288x^3 + 106x^2 - 17x + 1$.
What are the roots of $p(x)$?

4. PYRAMIDS The Great Pyramid in Giza, Egypt has a square base with side lengths of $5x$ yards and a height of $4x - 50$ yards. The volume of the Great Pyramid is 3,125,000 cubic yards. Use a calculator to find the value of x and the dimensions of the pyramid.

5. BOXES Devon made a box with length $x + 1$, width $x + 3$, and height $x - 3$.

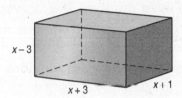

a. What is the volume of Devon's box as a function of x?

b. What is x if the volume of the box is equal to 1001 cubic inches?

c. What is x if the volume of the box is equal to $14\frac{5}{8}$ cubic inches?

Lesson 6-8

6-8 Enrichment

Irrational Numbers

Philosopher Hippasus of Metapontum was believed to have discovered that $\sqrt{2}$ was irrational. Mathematicians of the time denied the existence of irrational numbers and killed Hippasus, not wishing to believe this fundamental number could fail to be a ratio of integers.

The typical way to prove that $\sqrt{2}$ is irrational is by contradiction and relies on a few other common facts that are easily proven. That is, the proof assumes that it is rational and deduces a contradiction.

Theorem: $\sqrt{2}$ is irrational

Proof: Suppose $\sqrt{2}$ is a rational number. Then $\sqrt{2} = \frac{a}{b}$, where a and b are relatively prime integers. Relatively prime integers are integers that have no common factor other than one, therefore $\frac{a}{b}$ is a fraction written in lowest terms. It is also this condition that provides the contradiction. If we square both sides of the equation, $\sqrt{2} = \frac{a}{b}$, we have $2 = \frac{a^2}{b^2}$. This is equivalent to $a^2 = 2b^2$. However, this says that a^2 is an even number, thus a is an even number. If a is even and $\frac{a^2}{2} = b^2$, b is also even. Thus a and b have a factor in common other than one, namely two, and are not relatively prime. Hence $\sqrt{2}$ is irrational.

The Rational Zero Theorem provides a direct proof method.

Exercises

1. Use the rational zero theorem to prove that $\sqrt{2}$ is irrational.

2. Show that the square of an even number is even.

3. Show that any integer zeros of a polynomial function must be factors of the constant term a_0.

6-8 Graphing Calculator Activity

Rational Root Theorem

The following program performs synthetic division and displays the depressed polynomial coefficients in rational form. The program will allow the testing of possible rational zeros of a polynomial function.

PROGRAM: SYNTHDIV

Disp "DEGREE OF DIVIDEND"	P+1→P	Q→L_2(P)
Input M	Disp "COEFFICIENT"	P+1→P
Disp "COEFFICIENTS?"	Input A	If P≤M+1
Disp "0=SAME"	A→L_1(P)	Goto 3
Disp "1=QUOTIENT"	If P<M+1	Stop
Disp "2=NEW"	Goto 1	Lbl 4
Input U	Lbl 2	0→P
Disp "POSSIBLE ROOT"	1→P	Lbl 5
Input R	0→S	1+P→P
If U=0	Lbl 3	L_2(P)→L_1(P)
Goto 2	L_1(P) →F	If P<M+1
If U=1	F+S→Q	Goto 5
Goto 4	Disp Q ▶ Frac	Goto 2
0→P	Pause	
Lbl 1	RQ→S	

Example Find all of the rational zeros of $f(x) = 2x^3 - 11x^2 + 12x + 9$.

Use the program to test possible zeros. Test the zero 9 first.

Keystrokes: PRGM ▼ [SYNTHDIV] ENTER   ENTER 3 ENTER 2
ENTER 1 ENTER 2 ENTER (−) 11 ENTER 12 ENTER 9 ENTER .
Press ENTER until the screen displays **Done**.

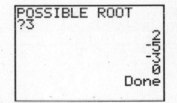

The column of numbers are the coefficients of the depressed polynomial.
Since the last number is not zero, 9 is not a solution. Test −1. Press ENTER
3 ENTER . Choose 0 for the same coefficients. Press ENTER (−) 1 then ENTER
until finished. Repeat this until a zero is found. Then press ENTER 2 for the
degree of the depressed polynomial and ENTER 1 for the quotient.

The zeros are 3, 3, and $-\frac{1}{2}$.

Exercises

Find all the rational zeros of each function.

1. $f(x) = x^3 - 8x^2 - 23x + 30$

2. $f(x) = x^3 - 7x^2 + 2x + 40$

3. $f(x) = 2x^3 - x^2 - 32x + 16$

4. $f(x) = x^4 + x^3 - 11x^2 - 9x + 18$

5. $p(x) = 3x^4 + 11x^3 + 11x^2 + x - 2$

6. $p(x) = x^4 - 2x^3 + x^2 - 8x - 12$

7. $p(x) = 3x^5 + x^4 - 243x - 81$

8. $p(x) = 3x^4 + 13x^3 + 15x^2 - 4$

6 Student Recording Sheet

Use this recording sheet with pages 338–339 of the Student Edition.

Multiple Choice

Read each question. Then fill in the correct answer.

1. Ⓐ Ⓑ Ⓒ Ⓓ

2. Ⓕ Ⓖ Ⓗ Ⓙ

3. Ⓐ Ⓑ Ⓒ Ⓓ

4. Ⓕ Ⓖ Ⓗ Ⓙ

5. Ⓐ Ⓑ Ⓒ Ⓓ

6. Ⓕ Ⓖ Ⓗ Ⓙ

7. Ⓐ Ⓑ Ⓒ Ⓓ

8. Ⓕ Ⓖ Ⓗ Ⓙ

9. Ⓐ Ⓑ Ⓒ Ⓓ

Short Response/Gridded Response

Record your answer in the blank.

For gridded response questions, also enter your answer in the grid by writing each number or symbol in a box. Then fill in the corresponding circle for that number or symbol.

10. _____ (grid in)

11. _____

12. _____

13. _____ (grid in)

14. _____ (grid in)

15. _____

Extended Response

Record your answers for Question 16 and 17 on the back of this paper.

Assessment

6 Rubric for Scoring Extended Response

General Scoring Guidelines

- If a student gives only a correct numerical answer to a problem but does not show how he or she arrived at the answer, the student will be awarded only 1 credit. All extended response questions require the student to show work.

- A fully correct answer for a multiple-part question requires correct responses for all parts of the question. For example, if a question has three parts, the correct response to one or two parts of the question that required work to be shown is *not* considered a fully correct response.

- Students who use trial and error to solve a problem must show their method. Merely showing that the answer checks or is correct is *not* considered a complete response for full credit.

Exercises 11 Rubric

Score	Specific Criteria
4	For Exercise 16, the polynomial equation for part **a** is written in the correct form ($h^2 + 2h^2 - 3h - 864 = 0$). For part **b**, all of the possible roots are listed, all of the factors of 864 ($\pm1, \pm2, \pm3, \pm4, \pm6, \pm8, \pm9, \pm12, \pm16, \pm18, \pm24, \pm27, \pm32, \pm36, \pm48, \pm54, \pm72, \pm96, \pm108, \pm144, \pm216, \pm288, \pm423, \pm864$). For part **c**, the equation is solved not only for h (9 cm) but also for each dimension (height = 9 cm, length = 8 cm, and width = 12 cm).
	For Exercise 17, a method is chosen for part **a** and explained fully. Any method used will give a relative maximum ($h \approx 160$). The relative maximum is used in part **b** to solve for t ($t \approx 5.7$).
3	A generally correct solution, but may contain minor flaws in reasoning or computation.
2	A partially correct interpretation and/or solution to the problem.
1	A correct solution with no evidence or explanation.
0	An incorrect solution indicating no mathematical understanding of the concept or task, or no solution given.

6   Chapter 6 Quiz 1

SCORE _____

(Lessons 6-1 and 6-2)

Simplify. Assume that no variable equals 0.

1. $(4n^2y^2)(-6n^2y^5)$

2. $\dfrac{16(x^3y)^2}{2(xy^0)^4}$

3. $(4x^5 + x^3 - 7x^2 + 2)(3x - 1)$

Simplify.

4. $(12x^3 - 16x^2y + 3xy^2 + 9y^2)(2x^{-3}y)^{-1}$

5. $(3p + 5r) + (6p - 4r)$

6. $(2x - 3) - (5x - 6)$ 7. $(4x - 5)(2x + 7)$

8. **MULTIPLE CHOICE** Which expression is equal to $(30a^2 - 11a + 15)(5a - 6)^{-1}$?

   A $6a + 5 + \dfrac{45}{5a - 6}$ **C** $6a - 5 - \dfrac{45}{5a + 6}$

   B $6a + 5$ **D** $-6a - 5 + \dfrac{45}{5a - 6}$

Simplify.

9. $(m^2 + m - 6) \div (m + 4)$

10. $(a^3 - 6a^2 + 10a - 3) \div (a - 3)$

1. _____

2. _____

3. _____

4. _____

5. _____

6. _____

7. _____

8. _____

9. _____

10. _____

----

6   Chapter 6 Quiz 2

SCORE _____

(Lessons 6-3 and 6-4)

1. If $p(x) = 3x^2 - 2x + 1$, find $p(-4)$.

1. _____

2. Determine whether the graph at the right represents an odd-degree polynomial or an even-degree polynomial function. Then state the number of real zeros.

2. _____

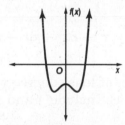

3. Graph $f(x) = x^3 - 5x^2 + 4x + 3$ by making a table of values. Then determine consecutive values of x between which each real zero is located. Estimate the x-coordinates at which the relative maxima and relative minima occur.

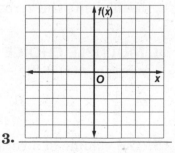

3. _____

State the degree and leading coefficient of each polynomial.

4. $8x^2 + 2x - 9$ 5. 235

4. _____

5. _____

Assessment

6 Chapter 6 Quiz 3

(Lessons 6-5 through 6-6)

SCORE _____

1. Factor $6a^2 - 3a - 18$ completely. If it is not factorable write *prime*.

1. _____

2. Solve $x^4 - 14x^2 + 45 = 0$.

2. _____

3. **MULTIPLE CHOICE** The sides of a square garden are x^2 yards long. The area inside the garden is 49 square yards. What is the value of x?

   A 49 yards

   B 7 yards

   C $\sqrt{7}$ yards

   D 2 yards

3. _____

4. Use synthetic substitution to find $f(3)$ and $f(-4)$ for $f(x) = x^4 - 8x - 11$.

4. _____

5. One factor of $x^3 + x^2 - 14x - 24$ is $x - 4$. Find the remaining factors.

5. _____

- -

6 Chapter 6 Quiz 4

(Lessons 6-7 and 6-8)

SCORE _____

1. State the possible number of positive real zeros, negative real zeros, and imaginary zeros for $g(x) = 3x^5 - 2x^3 - 4x^2 + 8x - 1$.

1. _____

2. Find all of the zeros of $f(x) = x^3 - 5x^2 + 8x - 6$.

2. _____

3. Write a polynomial function of least degree with integral coefficients the zeros of which include 4 and $1 - i$.

3. _____

4. **MULTIPLE CHOICE** Which of the following is a rational zeros of $h(x) = 2x^4 - 5x^3 + 3x^2 + 4x - 6$.

   A $\frac{1}{2}$ B 1   C $\frac{3}{2}$ D 2

4. _____

5. The volume of a rectangular solid is 540 cubic feet. The width is 3 feet more than the height, and the length is 4 more feet than the height. Find the dimensions of the solid.

5. _____

6 Chapter 6 Mid-Chapter Test

SCORE _____

(Lessons 6-1 through 6-4)

Part I Write the letter for the correct answer in the blank at the right of each question.

1. Simplify $(5x^3y)^2(-2x^5y^1)$.

   A $-50x^{10}y^3$ **B** $\dfrac{-50x^{11}}{y}$ **C** $-50x^{11}y^3$ **D** $-10x^3y^3$ 1. _____

2. Simplify $(x^2 + 2x - 5) - (3x^2 - 4x + 7)$.

   F $2x^2 - 2x - 12$ **G** $-2x^2 + 6x - 12$ **H** $4x^2 - 2x + 2$ **J** $4x^2 + 6x + 2$ 2. _____

3. Find $p(-4)$ if $p(x) = 3x^2 - 4x + 7$.

   A 7   **B** 71   **C** 57   **D** 39   3. _____

4. State the degree of $2x^2 - 5x^3 + 7x^4 - 9$.

   F 4   **G** 7   **H** -9   **J** 3   4. _____

For Questions 5 and 6, use the graph shown.

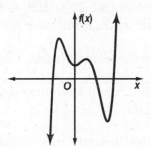

5. State the number of real zeros of the function.

   A 2   **C** 1

   B 4   **D** 3   5. _____

6. As $x \to +\infty$, $f(x) \to \underline{\ ?\ }$ describes the end behavior of the graph.

   F $-\infty$ **G** 0   **H** $+\infty$ **J** x 6. _____

Part II

7. Graph $f(x) = x^3 + 4x^2 - 5$ by using a table of values. Then determine consecutive integral values of x between which each real zero is located.

   7. _____

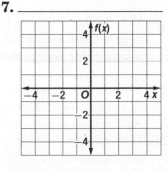

8. Use long division to find $(2x^3 - 7x^2 + 7x - 2) \div (x - 2)$.

   8. _____

9. Use synthetic division to find $(x^3 + 2x^2 - 34x + 9) \div (x + 7)$.

   9. _____

10. Simplify $(x^3 + 8) \div (x + 2)$

   10. _____

11. Simplify $(c + 3)(c - 4)$.

   11. _____

Assessment

6 — Chapter 6 Vocabulary Test

SCORE _____

degree of a polynomial	polynomial in one variable	simplify
depressed polynomial	power function	synthetic division
end behavior	prime polynomials	synthetic substitution
extrema	quadratic form	turning points
leading coefficient	relative maximum	
polynomial function	relative minimum	

Underline the correct word or phase that best completes each sentence.

1. (*End behavior, Synthetic substitution*) is a method for evaluating a polynomial function $f(x)$ at a particular value of x.

2. A (*relative maximum, depressed polynomial*) is a turning point where the graph increases as it approaches the point and decreases as it moves away from the point.

3. Writing the polynomial $2x^4 + 9x^2 - 15$ as $2(x^2)^2 - 9(x^2) - 15$ uses the idea of (*leading coefficients, quadratic form*).

4. To (*simplify, synthetic substitute*) $(3x^2y^2)(-2x^2y^3)$ means to write it as $-6x^4y^5$.

5. A shortcut method used to divide polynomials by binomials is called (*end behavior, synthetic division*).

6. The form we usually write in is called (*standard notation, quadratic form*).

7. If a point is on a graph of a polynomial function and no other nearby points of the graph have a lesser y-coordinate, the point is a relative (*maximum, minimum*) of the function.

8. If $x^3 + 3x^2 - 4x - 12$ is divided by $x - 2$, the quotient will be $x^2 + 5x + 6$ and the remainder will be 0. In this case, $x^2 + 5x + 6$ is called the (*quadratic form, depressed polynomial*).

9. The degree and (*relative minimum, leading coefficient*) of a polynomial function determines the graph's end behavior.

10. The expression $4x^3 + 3x^2 - 5x + 6$ is a(n) (*polynomial function, polynomial in one variable*).

Define each term in your own words.

11. end behavior

12. degree of a polynomial

6   Chapter 6 Test, Form 1   SCORE _____

Write the letter for the correct answer in the blank at the right of each question.

1. Simplify $(3x^0)^2(2x^4)$.

  A x^4 **B** $12x^4$ **C** $18x^6$ **D** $18x^4$ 1. _____

2. Simplify $\dfrac{3y^2z}{15y^5}$. Assume that no variable equals 0.

  F $\dfrac{z}{5y^3}$ **G** $\dfrac{y^3z}{5}$ **H** $5y^3z$ **J** $\dfrac{y^7z}{5}$ 2. _____

3. Shen is simplifying the expression $(3x^4 + 4x^2)(x^3 - 2x^2 - 1)$. Which of the following shows the correct product?

  A $3x^{12} - 6x^8 + 4x^6 - 11x^4 - 4x^2$ **C** $3x^7 + 6x^6 - 4x^5 + 11x^4 + 4x^2$

  B $3x^7 - 6x^6 + 4x^5 - 11x^4 - 4x^2$ **D** $3x^{12} - 6x^8 - 11x^4 + 4x^6 - 4x^2$ 3. _____

4. Simplify $(5m - 9) + (4m + 2)$.

  F $9m - 11$ **G** $m - 11$ **H** $9m - 7$ **J** $20m^2 - 18$ 4. _____

5. Simplify $3x(2x^2 - y)$.

  A $5x^3 + 3xy$ **B** $12x - y$ **C** $6x^2 - 3y$ **D** $6x^3 - 3xy$ 5. _____

6. Simplify $(x^2 - 2x - 35) \div (x + 5)$.

  F $x^2 - x - 30$ **H** $x - 7$

  G $x + 5$ **J** $x^3 + 3x^2 - 45x - 175$ 6. _____

7. Which represents the correct synthetic division of $(x^2 - 4x + 7) \div (x - 2)$?

  A
$$\begin{array}{r|rrr} -2 & 1 & -4 & 7 \\ & & -2 & 12 \\ \hline & 1 & -6 & 19 \end{array}$$
    C
$$\begin{array}{r|rrr} -2 & 1 & -4 & 7 \\ & & -2 & -16 \\ \hline & 1 & 8 & -9 \end{array}$$

  B
$$\begin{array}{r|rrr} 2 & 1 & -4 & 7 \\ & & 2 & 4 \\ \hline & 1 & -2 & 11 \end{array}$$
    D
$$\begin{array}{r|rrr} 2 & 1 & -4 & 7 \\ & & 2 & -4 \\ \hline & 1 & -2 & 3 \end{array}$$
    7. _____

8. Factor $m^2 + 9m + 14$ completely.

  F $m(m + 23)$ **H** $(m + 14)(m + 1)$

  G $(m + 7)(m + 2)$ **J** $m(m + 9) + 14$ 8. _____

9. Simplify $\dfrac{t^2 + t - 6}{t - 2}$. Assume that the denominator is not equal to 0.

  A $t - 5$ **B** $t - 2$ **C** $t - 3$ **D** $t + 3$ 9. _____

Assessment

6 **Chapter 6 Test, Form 1** *(continued)*

10. Find $p(-3)$ if $p(x) = 4 - x$.

    F 12   **G** 4   **H** 1   **J** 7

    10. _____

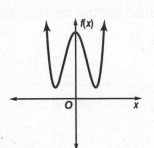

11. State the number of real zeros for the function whose graph is shown at the right.

    A 0   **C** 2

    B 1   **D** 3

    11. _____

For Questions 12 and 13, use the graph shown at the right.

12. Determine the values of x between which a real zero is located.

    F between -1 and 0

    G between 6 and 7

    H between -2 and -1

    J between 2 and 3

    12. _____

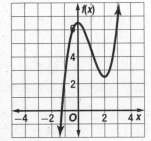

13. Estimate the x-coordinate at which a relative minimum occurs.

    A 3   **B** 2   **C** 0   **D** -1

    13. _____

14. Write the expression $x^4 + 5x^2 - 8$ in quadratic form, if possible.

    F $(x^2)^2 + 5(x^2) - 8$ **H** $(x^4)^2 + 5(x^4) - 8$

    G $(x^2)^2 - 5(x^2) - 8$ **J** not possible

    14. _____

15. Solve $x^4 - 13x^2 + 36 = 0$.

    A $-3, -2, 2, 3$ **B** $-9, -4, 4, 9$ **C** $2, 3, 2i, 3i$ **D** $-2, -3, 2i, 3i$ 15. _____

16. Use synthetic substitution to find $f(3)$ for $f(x) = x^2 - 9x + 5$.

    F -23 **G** -16 **H** -13 **J** 41

    16. _____

17. One factor of $x^3 + 4x^2 - 11x - 30$ is $x + 2$. Find the remaining factors.

    A $x - 5, x + 3$ **B** $x - 3, x + 5$ **C** $x - 6, x + 5$ **D** $x - 5, x + 6$ 17. _____

18. Which describes the number and type of roots of the equation $4x + 7 = 0$?

    F 1 imaginary root   **H** 1 real root and 1 imaginary root

    G 2 real roots   **J** 1 real root

    18. _____

19. Which is *not* a root of the equation $x^3 - x^2 - 10x - 8 = 0$?

    A 1   **B** 4   **C** -2 **D** -1

    19. _____

20. Find all the rational zeros of $p(x) = x^3 - 12x - 16$.

    F $-2, 4$ **G** $2, -4$ **H** 4   **J** -2

    20. _____

Bonus Find the value of k so that $x - 3$ divides
$2x^3 - 11x^2 + 19x + k$ with no remainder.

B: _____

6   **Chapter 6 Test, Form 2A**   SCORE _____

Write the letter for the correct answer in the blank at the right of each question.

1. Simplify $(3a^0b^2)(2a^3b^2)^2$.

   A $12a^6b^6$ **B** $36a^6b^8$ **C** $6b^8$ **D** $12ab^6$ 1. _____

2. Simplify $\dfrac{4a^4\,b^2\,c}{12a^2\,b^5\,c^3}$. Assume that no variable equals 0.

   F $\dfrac{a^2\,b^3}{8c^2}$ **G** $\dfrac{a^2\,b^3}{3c^2}$ **H** $\dfrac{a^2\,c^2}{3b^3}$ **J** $\dfrac{a^2}{3b^3c^2}$ 2. _____

3. Max is simplifying the expression $(2x^5 - 5x^3)(x^4 + 3x^2 - 4)$. Which of the following shows the correct product?

   A $2x^9 - x^7 + 23x^5 - 20x^3$ **C** $2x^9 - x^7 + 23x^5 - 20x^3$

   B $2x^{20} - 6x^{10} + 8x^5 + 5x^{12} + 15x^6 - 20x^3$ **D** $2x^9 + x^7 - 23x^5 + 20x^3$ 3. _____

4. Simplify $(3a^3 - 7a^2 + a) - (6a^3 - 4a^2 - 8)$.

   F $-3a^6 - 3a^4 + a + 8$ **H** $-3a^3 - 11a^2 + a - 8$

   G $-3a^6 - 11a^4 + a - 8$ **J** $-3a^3 - 3a^2 + a + 8$ 4. _____

5. Simplify $(7m - 8)^2$.

   A $49m^2 + 64$ **C** $49m^2 - 112m + 64$

   B $49m^2 - 64$ **D** $49m^2 - 30m + 64$ 5. _____

6. Simplify $(4x^3 - 2x^2 + 8x + 8) \div (2x + 1)$.

   F $2x^2 - 2x + 5 + \dfrac{3}{2x + 1}$ **H** $2x^2 + 4 - \dfrac{9}{2x + 1}$

   G $2x^2 + 4 - \dfrac{12}{2x + 1}$ **J** $x^2 - 4x + 6 - \dfrac{14}{2x + 1}$ 6. _____

7. Which represents the correct synthetic division of $(2x^3 - 5x + 40) \div (x + 3)$?

   A
$$
\begin{array}{r|rrr}
-3 & 2 & -5 & 40 \\
   &   & -6 & 33 \\
\hline
   & 2 & -11 & 73
\end{array}
$$

   C
$$
\begin{array}{r|rrrr}
-3 & 2 & 0 & -5 & 40 \\
   &   & -6 & 18 & -39 \\
\hline
   & 2 & -6 & 13 & 1
\end{array}
$$

   B
$$
\begin{array}{r|rrr}
3 & 2 & -5 & 40 \\
  &   & 6 & 3 \\
\hline
  & 2 & 1 & 43
\end{array}
$$

   D
$$
\begin{array}{r|rrrr}
3 & 2 & 0 & -5 & 40 \\
  &   & 6 & 18 & 39 \\
\hline
  & 2 & 6 & 13 & 79
\end{array}
$$

     7. _____

8. Factor $y^3 - 64$ completely.

   F $(y - 4)^3$ **H** $(y - 4)(y^2 + 4y + 16)$

   G $(y - 4)(y + 4)^2$ **J** $(y - 4)(y^2 - 4y + 16)$ 8. _____

9. Find $p(-4)$ if $p(x) = 3x^3 - 2x^2 + 6x - 4$.

   A -252 **B** -140 **C** 132 **D** 180 9. _____

Assessment

6 **Chapter 6 Test, Form 2A** *(continued)*

10. If $r(x) = x^3 - 2x + 1$, find $r(2a^3)$.

    F $8a^6 - 4a^3 + 1$ **G** $4a^6 + 4a^3 + 1$ **H** $6a^6 - 4a^3 + 1$ **J** $8a^9 - 4a^3 + 1$ **10.** _____

11. State the number of real zeros for the function whose graph is shown at the right.

    A 0   **C** 3

    B 2   **D** 1   **11.** _____

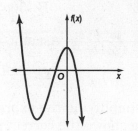

For Questions 12 and 13, use the graph shown.

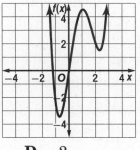

12. Determine the values of x between which a real zero is located.

    F between 1 and 2   **H** between -4 and -3

    G between -2 and -1 **J** between 2 and 3   **12.** _____

13. Estimate the x-coordinate at which a relative maximum occurs.

    A 1   **B** -1 **C** 2   **D** -2 **13.** _____

14. Write the expression $10x^8 - 6x^4 - 20$ in quadratic form, if possible.

    F $10(x^4)^2 - 6(x^2)^2 - 20$ **H** $10(x^4)^2 - 6(x^4) - 20$

    G $10(x^2)^4 - 6(x^2)^2 - 20$ **J** not possible   **14.** _____

15. Solve $x^4 - 6x^2 - 27 = 0$.

    A $\sqrt{3}, 3, 3i, i\sqrt{3}$ **C** $-3, 3, i\sqrt{3}, -i\sqrt{3}$

    B $-3, -\sqrt{3}, \sqrt{3}, 3$ **D** $-\sqrt{3}, 3, 3i, -3i$ **15.** _____

16. Use synthetic substitution to find $f(-2)$ for $f(x) = 2x^4 - 3x^3 + x^2 - x + 5$.

    F 15   **G** 67   **H** 63   **J** 19   **16.** _____

17. One factor of $x^3 - 3x^2 - 4x + 12$ is $x + 2$. Find the remaining factors.

    A $x + 2, x + 3$ **B** $x + 2, x - 3$ **C** $x - 2, x + 3$ **D** $x - 2, x - 3$ **17.** _____

18. Which describes the number and type of roots of the equation $x^4 - 64 = 0$?

    F 2 real roots, 2 imaginary roots   **H** 4 real roots

    G 3 real roots, 1 imaginary root   **J** 4 imaginary roots   **18.** _____

19. State the possible number of imaginary zeros of $f(x) = 7x^3 - x^2 + 10x - 4$.

    A exactly 1   **B** exactly 3   **C** 3 or 1   **D** 2 or 0   **19.** _____

20. Find all the rational zeros of $f(x) = 4x^3 - 3x^2 - 22x - 15$.

    F $\pm\frac{5}{2}, \pm1, \pm3$ **G** $-\frac{5}{4}, -1, 3$ **H** 1, 3   **J** $-5, -1, 3$ **20.** _____

Bonus Find the value of k so that $9x^3 - 2x^2 + kx + 6 \div (x + 2)$ has a remainder of 8.   **B:** _____

6   Chapter 6 Test, Form 2B   SCORE _____

Write the letter for the correct answer in the blank at the right of each question.

1. Simplify $(3x^0y^4)(2x^2y)^3$.

   A $24x^6y^7$ **B** $216x^6y^5$ **C** $24x^5$ **D** $6x^6y^7$ 1. _____

2. Simplify $\dfrac{2x^2y^5z^4}{8x^6yz^3}$. Assume that no variable equals 0.

   F $\dfrac{y^4z^7}{4x^4}$ **G** $\dfrac{y^4z^2}{6x^4}$ **H** $\dfrac{y^4z}{4x^4}$ **J** $\dfrac{y^4z^7}{6x^4}$ 2. _____

3. Maria is simplifying the expression $(x^3 - 6x)(2x^3 + 5x - 1)$. Which of the following shows the correct product?

   A $2x^6 - 7x^4 - x^3 - 30x^2 + 6x$ **C** $2x^9 - 8x^3 - 30x^2 + 6x$

   B $2x^9 - 7x^4 - 11x^3 - 30x^2 + 6x$ **D** $2x^6 + 5x^4 - x^3 - 11x^2 - 6x$ 3. _____

4. Simplify $(7x^3 - 2x^2 + 3) + (x^2 - x - 5)$.

   F $7x^3 - 2x^2 - x - 2$ **H** $7x^3 - 3x^2 - 2$

   G $8x^5 - 3x^3 - 2$ **J** $7x^3 - x^2 - x - 2$ 4. _____

5. Simplify $(5x - 4)^2$.

   A $25x^2 - 16$ **C** $25x^2 - 40x + 16$

   B $25x^2 - 20x + 16$ **D** $25x^2 - 18x + 16$ 5. _____

6. Simplify $(6x^3 - 16x^2 + 11x - 5) \div (3x - 2)$.

   F $6x^2 - 12x + 3 - \dfrac{9}{3x - 2}$ **H** $2x^2 - 4x + 1 - \dfrac{3}{3x - 2}$

   G $2x^2 - 4x + 1 - \dfrac{1}{3x - 2}$ **J** $x^2 + 8x - 3 - \dfrac{9}{3x - 2}$ 6. _____

7. Which represents the correct synthetic division of $(3x^3 - 2x + 5) \div (x - 2)$?

   A

2	3	−2	5
		6	8
	3	4	13

   C

2	3	0	2	5
		6	12	20
	3	6	10	25

   B

−2	3	−2	5
		−6	16
	3	−8	21

   D

−2	3	0	−2	5
		−6	12	−20
	3	−6	10	−15

     7. _____

8. Factor $27x^3 - 1$ completely.

   F $(3x - 1)(9x^2 + 3x + 1)$ **H** $(3x - 1)(9x^2 - 3x - 1)$

   G $(3x - 1)^3$ **J** $(3x - 1)(9x^2 - 3x + 1)$ 8. _____

9. Find $p(-3)$ if $p(x) = 4x^3 - 5x^2 + 7x - 10$.

   A -94 **B** 32 **C** -184 **D** -142 9. _____

Assessment

6 **Chapter 6 Test, Form 2B** *(continued)*

10. If $r(x) = 4x^2 - 3x + 7$, find $r(3a^2)$.

    F $36a^4 - 9a^2 + 7$ **H** $144a^4 - 9a^2 + 7$

    G $36a^4 + 9a^2 + 7$ **J** $12a^4 - 9a^2 + 7$ 10. _____

11. State the number of real zeros for the function whose graph is shown.

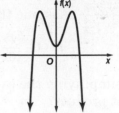

    A 1   **C** 3

    B 4   **D** 2   11. _____

For Questions 12 and 13, use the graph shown.

12. Determine the values of x between which a real zero is located.

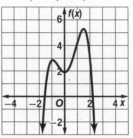

    F between -2 and -1 **H** between 0 and 1

    G between -1 and 0   **J** between -3 and -2 12. _____

13. Estimate the x-coordinate at which a relative minimum occurs.

    A -1 **B** 0   **C** 1   **D** 2   13. _____

14. Write the expression $9n^6 + 7n^3 - 6$ in quadratic form, if possible.

    F $9(n^3)^3 + 7(n^3) - 6$ **H** $9(n^2)^3 + 7(n^2) - 6$

    G $9(n^3)^2 + 7(n^3) - 6$ **J** not possible   14. _____

15. Solve $b^4 + 2b^2 - 24 = 0$.

    A $-2, -\sqrt{6}, \sqrt{6}, 2$ **C** $-2, 2, -i\sqrt{6}, i\sqrt{6}$

    B $-\sqrt{6}, 2, 2i, i\sqrt{6}$ **D** $-2i, 2i, -\sqrt{6}, \sqrt{6}$ 15. _____

16. Use synthetic substitution to find $f(-3)$ for $f(x) = x^4 - 4x^3 + 2x^2 - 4x + 6$.

    F 9   **G** 225   **H** 201   **J** -15 16. _____

17. One factor of $x^3 + 2x^2 - 11x - 12$ is $x + 4$. Find the remaining factors.

    A $x + 1, x + 3$ **B** $x - 1, x + 3$ **C** $x + 1, x - 3$ **D** $x - 1, x - 3$ 17. _____

18. Which describes the number and type of roots of the equation $x^3 + 121x = 0$?

    F 1 real root, 2 imaginary roots   **H** 2 real roots, 1 imaginary root

    G 3 real roots   **J** 3 imaginary roots   18. _____

19. State the possible number of imaginary zeros of $g(x) = x^4 + 3x^3 + 7x^2 - 6x - 13$.

    A 3 or 1   **B** 2 or 0   **C** exactly 1   **D** exactly 3   19. _____

20. Find all the rational zeros of $g(x) = 2x^3 - 11x^2 + 8x + 21$.

    F $-1, 3, \frac{7}{2}$ **G** $\pm 1, \pm 3, \pm\frac{7}{2}$ **H** $-1, 3$ **J** $-1, 3, 7$ 20. _____

Bonus Factor $x^2z^2 + 36y^2 - 4y^2z^2 - 9x^2$ completely.   **B:** _____

6   Chapter 6 Test, Form 2C   SCORE _____

Simplify. Assume that no variable equals 0.

1. $(5r^2t)^2(3r^0t^4)$ 2. $\dfrac{2a^4bc^5}{18a^2b^7c^1}$

1. _____

2. _____

For Questions 3–5, simplify.

3. $(4c^2 - 12c + 7) - (c^2 + 2c - 5)$ 4. $(3x + 4)(2x - 5)$

3. _____

4. _____

5. $(9p^2 + 7p) + (5p^2 - 4p - 12)$

5. _____

6. Simplify $(12k^7 + 4k^5 - k^2)(2k^2 - 3)$.

6. _____

7. **MONEY** A pancake breakfast fundraiser served 400 people and charged \$5 for adults and \$3.50 for children. Use x to represent the number of adults served and write an expression to show how much money was raised. Then simplify the expression.

7. _____

8. Use long division to find $(10y^3 - 9y^2 + 6y - 10) \div (2y + 3)$.

8. _____

9. Use synthetic division to find $(x^3 + 4x^2 - 17x - 50) \div (x + 3)$.

9. _____

10. Factor $2xz - 3yz + 8x - 12y$ completely. If the polynomial is not factorable, write *prime*.

10 _____

11. Find $p(-5)$ if $p(x) = x^3 - 2x^2 + x + 4$.

11. _____

12. Find $p(x + 1)$ if $p(x) = x^2 - 3x - 1$.

12. _____

For Questions 13–15, use the graph shown.

13. Describe the end behavior.

13. _____

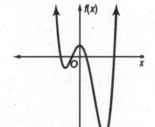

14. Determine whether the graph represents an odd-degree or an even-degree polynomial function.

14. _____

15. State the number of real zeros.

15. _____

Assessment

16. The path of a mouse running on a tiled floor can be modeled by the graph of $f(x) = x^3 - 3x + 1$. Graph $f(x) = x^3 - 3x + 1$ by making a table of values. Then determine consecutive values of x between which each real zero is located.

16. _____

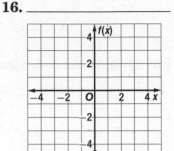

17. For the graph in Question 16, estimate the x-coordinates at which the relative maxima and relative minima occur.

17. _____

18. Write the expression $9n^6 - 36n^3$ in quadratic form, if possible.

18. _____

19. Solve $x^4 - 12x^2 - 45 = 0$.

19. _____

20. Use synthetic substitution to find $f(-4)$ for $f(x) = x^3 + 3x^2 - 5x - 7$.

20. _____

21. One factor of $x^3 + 2x^2 - 23x - 60$ is $x + 4$. Find the remaining factors.

21. _____

22. State the possible number of positive real zeros, negative real zeros, and imaginary zeros for $f(x) = 3x^4 - 2x^3 - 5x^2 + 6x - 2$.

22. _____

23. The height of a box that Carol is wrapping is 7 inches more than the width of the box. The length is 2 inches less than twice the width. The volume of the box is 1,680 cubic inches. What are the dimensions of the box?

23. _____

24. List all of the possible rational zeros of $f(x) = 2x^3 + x^2 - 4x + 8$.

24. _____

25. Find all of the rational zeros of $g(x) = 2x^3 - x^2 - 7x + 6$.

25. _____

Bonus Simplify $\dfrac{x^2 - 36}{x^2 + 2x - 24}$. Assume that the denominator is not equal to 0.

B: _____

6   Chapter 6 Test, Form 2D   SCORE _____

Simplify. Assume that no variable equals 0.

1. $(2c^2d^0)^3(5c^7d^2)$

2. $\dfrac{12a^2b^4c^5}{48a^6b^3c^3}$

1. _____

2. _____

For Questions 3–5, simplify.

3. $(3f^2 + 5f - 9) + (4f^2 - 7f + 12)$ 4. $(5m - 6)(2m + 1)$

3. _____

4. _____

5. $(6g^3 - 2g + 1) - (3g^2 + 5g - 7)$

5. _____

6. Simplify $(11k^2 + 10k^3 - 4k^2)(3k^2 - 2k)$.

6. _____

7. **MONEY** A spaghetti dinner fundraiser served 500 people and charged \$7 for adults and \$4.50 for children. Use x to represent the number of adults served and write an expression to show how much money was raised. Then simplify the expression.

7. _____

8. Use long division to find $(8x^3 - 10x^2 + 9x - 10) \div (2x - 1)$.

8. _____

9. Use synthetic division to find $(x^3 + 4x^2 - 9x + 10) \div (x - 2)$.

9. _____

10. Factor $20x^2 - 8x + 5xy - 2y$ completely. If the polynomial is not factorable, write *prime*.

10. _____

11. Find $p(-4)$ if $p(x) = x^3 - 3x^2 + 7x + 6$.

11. _____

12. Find $p(x + 1)$ if $p(x) = x^2 - 4x + 2$.

12. _____

For Questions 13–15, use the graph shown.

13. Describe the end behavior.

13. _____

14. Determine whether the graph represents an odd-degree or an even-degree polynomial function.

14. _____

15. State the number of real zeros.

15. _____

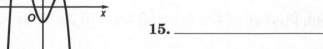

Assessment

6 **Chapter 6 Test, Form 2D** *(continued)*

16. Greta designed some water pipes whose shape can be modeled by the graph of $f(x) = -x^3 + 3x + 1$. Graph $f(x) = -x^3 + 3x + 1$ by making a table of values. Then determine consecutive values of x between which each real zero is located.

16. _____

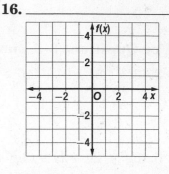

17. For the graph in Question 16, estimate the x-coordinates at which the relative maxima and relative minima occur.

17. _____

18. Write the expression $5x^{10} - 4x^5 + 3$ in quadratic form, if possible.

18. _____

19. Solve $x^4 - 4x^2 - 12 = 0$.

19. _____

20. Use synthetic substitution to find $f(-4)$ for $f(x) = x^4 - 7x^2 - 12$.

20. _____

21. One factor of $g(x) = x^3 + x^2 - 9x - 9$ is $x - 3$. Find the remaining factors.

21. _____

22. State the number of positive real zeros, negative real zeros, and imaginary zeros for $f(x) = 2x^4 - 5x^3 - 3x^2 + x + 6$.

22. _____

23. The height of a box that Bill is shipping is 4 inches less than the width of the box. The length is 10 inches more than twice the width. The volume of the box is 264 cubic inches. What are the dimensions of the box?

23. _____

24. List all of the possible rational zeros of $g(x) = 2x^3 + 2x^2 - 7x - 14$.

24. _____

25. Find all of the rational zeros of $h(x) = 3x^3 + 4x^2 - 13x + 6$.

25. _____

Bonus Simplify $\dfrac{x^2 - x - 20}{x^2 - 25}$. Assume that the denominator is not equal to 0.

B: _____

6   Chapter 6 Test, Form 3   SCORE _____

Simplify. Assume that no variable equals 0.

1. $\dfrac{(-2a^2)^2}{4a^2}$

2. $\dfrac{2x^2y^0(5xy^2)^2}{5(-2xy^2)}$

1. _____

2. _____

For Questions 3 and 4, simplify.

3. $\left(12p^2 - \dfrac{6}{5}r^2 + \dfrac{4}{3}pr\right) - (3pr + 2r^2)$

3. _____

4. $(m - 2p)^2$

4. _____

5. Simplify $(9k^6 + 8k^4 - 6k^2)(4k^2 - 5)$.

5. _____

6. **MONEY** A local fish fry fundraiser served 300 people and charged \$9 for adults and \$5.50 for children. Use x to represent the number of adults served and write an expression to show how much money was raised. Then simplify the expression.

6. _____

7. Use long division to find $\dfrac{x^4 + x^2 - 2x + 7}{x^2 - 3x + 1}$.

7. _____

8. Use synthetic division to find $\dfrac{2x^3 + x^2 + 1}{x + 1}$.

8. _____

For Questions 9 and 10, factor completely. If the polynomial is not factorable, Write *prime*.

9. $162w^4 - 2n^4$

10. $x^6 + 8y^6$

9. _____

10. _____

11. Solve $\dfrac{3}{7}x^2 + 5 = 0$

11. _____

12. Find $p(-2)$ if $p(x) = \dfrac{1}{8}x^3 + \dfrac{3}{4}x^2 - \dfrac{1}{2}x + \dfrac{4}{3}$.

12. _____

13. If $p(x) = 2x^2 - 3x + 1$ and $r(x) = x^2 - 5x$, find $r(x^2) - p(x + 1)$.

13. _____

14. Describe the end behavior and determine whether the graph represents an odd-degree or an even-degree polynomial function. Then state the number of real zeros.

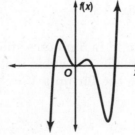

14. _____

Assessment

15. Clyde modified some water pipes so that the water flow could be modeled by the graph $f(x) = -x^4 + 3x^2 + x - 2$. Graph $f(x) = -x^4 + 3x^2 + x - 2$ by making a table of values. Then determine the values of x between which the real zeros are located.

15. _____

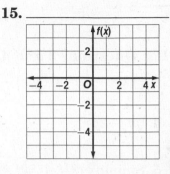

16. For the graph in Question 15, estimate the x-coordinates at which the relative maxima and relative minima occur.

16. _____

17. Write $9b^5 + 3b^3 - 8b$ in quadratic form, if possible.

17. _____

18. Solve $x^{\frac{1}{2}} - 5x^{\frac{1}{4}} + 6 = 0$.

18. _____

19. Use synthetic substitution to find $f(-4)$ for $f(x) = 2x^6 - 4x^4 + 2x^3 + 5x - 6$.

19. _____

20. Find the value of k so that the remainder is 3 for $(x^2 + x - k) \div (x + 1)$.

20. _____

21. State the possible number of positive real zeros, negative real zeros, and imaginary zeros for $f(x) = 2x^{10} - 3x^8 + 4x^6 - x^4 + 3x^2 - 2$.

21. _____

22. Find all of the zeros of the function $q(x) = x^4 - 8x^3 + 22x^2 - 8x - 39$.

22. _____

23. List all of the possible rational zeros of $h(x) = 9x^6 - 12x^3 + 15$.

23. _____

24. Find all of the rational zeros of $h(x) = 24x^4 - 38x^3 - 23x^2 + 5x + 2$.

24. _____

25. The height of a square pyramid is 5 meters shorter than the side of its base. Its volume is 108 cubic meters, how tall is the pyramid? Use the formula $V = \frac{1}{3}Bh$.

25. _____

Bonus If $f(-3) = -120$, for $f(x) = x^4 + x^3 - 19x^2 + kx + 30$, find $f(1)$.

B: _____

6   Chapter 6 Extended-Response Test   SCORE _____

Demonstrate your knowledge by giving a clear, concise solution to each problem. Be sure to include all relevant drawings and justify your answers. You may show your solutions in more than one way or investigate beyond the requirements of the problem.

1. The polynomial $2x^2 + 3x + 1$ can be represented by the tiles shown in the figure at the right.

These tiles can be arranged to form the rectangle shown. Notice that the area of the rectangle is $2x^2 + 3x + 1$ units².

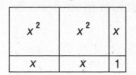

   a. Find the length and width of the rectangle.

   b. Explain how to find the perimeter of the rectangle. Then find the perimeter.

   c. Select a value for x and substitute that value into each of the expressions above. For your value of x, state the length, width, perimeter, and area of the rectangle. Discuss any restrictions on your choice of x.

   d. Factor the polynomial $2x^2 + 3x + 1$. Compare your answers to part **a.**

2. **a.** Sketch a graph of a polynomial function $f(x)$ of degree 5 that has the maximum number of real zeros possible for a function of its degree. Label the zeros $z_1, z_2, \ldots$.

   b. Label relative maximum points of the graph, if any, $A_1, A_2, \ldots$ and label relative minimum points of the graph, if any, $B_1, B_2, \ldots$.

   c. State the domain and range of the function.

   d. Use the notation "As $x \rightarrow$ ___ , $f(x) \rightarrow$ ___" to describe the end behavior of your graph.

3. **a.** Write a fourth-degree polynomial $P(x)$ where no coefficient is zero, that is $a_n \neq 0$ for any n.

   b. Find $P(-2)$ in two different ways.

   c. Determine whether $x + 1$ is a factor of $P(x)$.

   d. Explain what information Descartes' Rule of Signs provides about $P(x)$.

   e. Explain how to find, then list, all of the possible rational zeros of $P(x)$.

   f. Explain how to find, then state, the rational zeros of $P(x)$.

Assessment

6 Standardized Test Practice

SCORE _____

(Chapters 1–6)

Part 1: Multiple Choice
Instructions: Fill in the appropriate circle for the best answer.

1. In the figure, circle P represents all prime numbers, circle Q represents all numbers whose square roots are *not* integers, and circle R represents all multiples of 4. In which region does 24 belong?

    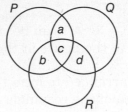

    A a **C** c

    B b **D** d

    1. Ⓐ Ⓑ Ⓒ Ⓓ

2. Find the reciprocal of $\frac{3}{x} + \frac{2}{5}$.

    F $\frac{2x + 15}{5x}$ **G** $\frac{5x}{6}$ **H** $\frac{5x}{2x + 15}$ **J** x

    2. Ⓕ Ⓖ Ⓗ Ⓙ

3. Suppose a set of data contains just two data items. If the median is w, the mean is x, and the mode is y, which of the following must be equal?

    A w, x, and y **B** x and y **C** w and x **D** w and y

    3. Ⓐ Ⓑ Ⓒ Ⓓ

4. What is the value of cd in the equation $32cd = 11cd - 42$?

    F $-\frac{1}{2}$ **G** $\frac{1}{2}$ **H** 2   **J** -2

    4. Ⓕ Ⓖ Ⓗ Ⓙ

5. Hoshiko owns one-fifth of a business. She sells her share for $15,000. What is the total value of the business?

    A $3000   **B** $75,000   **C** $100,000   **D** $150,000

    5. Ⓐ Ⓑ Ⓒ Ⓓ

6. If r is an odd integer and $m = 8r$, then $\frac{m}{2}$ will always be _____.

    F odd   **G** even   **H** positive   **J** negative

    6. Ⓕ Ⓖ Ⓗ Ⓙ

7. 13% of 160 is 16% of _____.

    A 13   **B** 130   **C** 1300   **D** 13,000

    7. Ⓐ Ⓑ Ⓒ Ⓓ

8. If $m^2 = 3$, then what is the value of $5m^6$?

    F 15   **G** 30   **H** 45   **J** 135

    8. Ⓕ Ⓖ Ⓗ Ⓙ

9. Which is the equation of a line that passes through a point with coordinates $(7, -1)$ and is perpendicular to the graph of $y + 2x = 1$?

    A $y = 2x - 15$ **B** $y = -2x + 13$ **C** $y = \frac{1}{2}x + 2\frac{1}{2}$ **D** $y = \frac{1}{2}x - 4\frac{1}{2}$

    9. Ⓐ Ⓑ Ⓒ Ⓓ

10. If $mn = 16$ and $m^2 + n^2 = 68$, then $(m + n)^2 = $ _____.

    F 68   **H** 84

    G 100   **J** cannot be determined

    10. Ⓕ Ⓖ Ⓗ Ⓙ

6 Standardized Test Practice *(continued)*

11. What is the value of $|a - b| + |b - a|$ if $a = b - \dfrac{1}{3}$?

   A $2b + \dfrac{2}{3}$ **B** $2b - \dfrac{2}{3}$ **C** $-\dfrac{2}{3}$ **D** $\dfrac{2}{3}$ 11. Ⓐ Ⓑ Ⓒ Ⓓ

12. If the shortest side of the triangle below measures 5 feet, what is the area of the triangle to the nearest square foot?

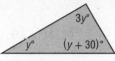

   F 44 ft²   **G** 43 ft²   **H** 22 ft²   **J** 21 ft²   12. Ⓕ Ⓖ Ⓗ Ⓙ

13. The circle is divided into eight sectors of equal area. In two consecutive spins, what is the probability of spinning a "50" and then spinning an odd-numbered region?

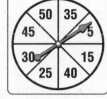

   A $\dfrac{5}{64}$ **B** $\dfrac{3}{4}$ **C** $\dfrac{1}{2}$ **D** $\dfrac{7}{8}$ 13. Ⓐ Ⓑ Ⓒ Ⓓ

14. A shelf in a lumber yard will safely hold up to 1000 pounds. A crate on the shelf is marked 270 pounds. What is the greatest number of sheets of plywood, each weighing 7 pounds, that may safely be stacked on the shelf?

   F 103   **G** 104   **H** 105   **J** 106   14. Ⓕ Ⓖ Ⓗ Ⓙ

15. At a school-sponsored car wash, the fees charged were: $5 per car, $8 per pickup truck, $10 per full-size van. Twice as many cars were washed as pickup trucks. The amount collected for washing cars and pickup trucks was $360. A total of $410 was collected at the car wash. Find the number of cars washed.

   A 40 cars   **B** 25 cars   **C** 20 cars   **D** 65 cars   15. Ⓐ Ⓑ Ⓒ Ⓓ

Part 2: Gridded Response

Instructions: Enter your answer by writing each digit of the answer in a column box and then shading in the appropriate circle that corresponds to that entry.

16. The volume of a cube with a surface area of 384 in² is _____ in³.

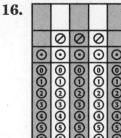

17. For all positive integers m, $\boxed{m} = 2m^2 + 1$. What is the value of x if $\boxed{x} = 45{,}001$?

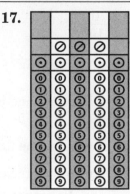

Assessment

6 Standardized Test Practice *(continued)*

Part 3: Short Response
Instructions: Write your answers in the space provided.

18. Write an algebraic expression to represent the verbal
expression *the square of the sum of a number and three*.

18. _____

19. If $f(x) = x^2 + 3x$, find $f(2 - a)$.

19. _____

20. Write an equation in slope-intercept form of the line
through $(1, 3)$ and $(-3, 7)$.

20. _____

21. Solve the system of equations $2x - 5y = 16$
$4x + 3y = 6$ by using elimination.

21. _____

22. The floor area of a furniture storeroom is 500 square yards.
One sofa requires 3 square yards and one dining table
requires 4 square yards of space. The room can hold a
maximum of 150 pieces of furniture. Let s represent
the number of sofas and t represent the number of tables.
Write a system of inequalities to represent the number of
pieces of furniture that can be placed in the storeroom.

22. _____

23. State the dimensions of matrix A if $A = \begin{bmatrix} 0 & 3 \\ 10 & 7 \\ 0 & -4 \end{bmatrix}$

23. _____

24. Find the product $\begin{bmatrix} 3 & 6 & 4 \\ 0 & -5 & 2 \end{bmatrix} \begin{bmatrix} 1 \\ 5 \\ -2 \end{bmatrix}$, if possible.

24. _____

25. Write a matrix equation for the system of equations
$3m - 2f = 16$
$4m + 5f = 9$

25. _____

26. Evaluate $\dfrac{2.4 \times 10^9}{1.6 \times 10^{-2}}$.

26. _____

27. Use long division to find $(6x^3 + x^2 + x) \div (2x + 1)$.

27. _____

28. Consider the polynomial function,
$f(x) = 2x^4 - x^3 + 6x^2 - 7x - 5$

   a. What is the degree of the function?

28a. _____

   b. What is the leading coefficient of the function?

28b. _____

   c. Evaluate $f(-2)$ and $f(3a)$.

28c. _____

NAME _____ DATE _____ PERIOD _____

6-1 Study Guide and Intervention

Operations with Polynomials

Multiply and Divide Monomials Negative exponents are a way of expressing the multiplicative inverse of a number.

Negative Exponents	$a^{-n} = \dfrac{1}{a^n}$ and $\dfrac{1}{a^{-n}} = a^n$ for any real number $a \neq 0$ and any integer n.

When you **simplify an expression**, you rewrite it without powers of powers, parentheses, or negative exponents. Each base appears only once, and all fractions are in simplest form. The following properties are useful when simplifying expressions.

Product of Powers	$a^m \cdot a^n = a^{m+n}$ for any real number a and integers m and n.
Quotient of Powers	$\dfrac{a^m}{a^n} = a^{m-n}$ for any real number $a \neq 0$ and integers m and n.
Properties of Powers	For a, b real numbers and m, n integers: $(a^m)^n = a^{mn}$ $(ab)^m = a^m b^m$ $\left(\dfrac{a}{b}\right)^n = \dfrac{a^n}{b^n}$, $b \neq 0$ $\left(\dfrac{a}{b}\right)^{-n} = \left(\dfrac{b}{a}\right)^n$ or $\dfrac{b^n}{a^n}$, $a \neq 0$, $b \neq 0$

Example   Simplify. Assume that no variable equals 0.

a. $(3m^4 n^{-2})(-5mn)^2$

$(3m^4 n^{-2})(-5mn)^2 = 3m^4 n^{-2} \cdot 25m^2 n^2$
$= 75 m^4 m^2 n^{-2} n^2$
$= 75 m^{4+2} n^{-2+2}$
$= 75 m^6$

b. $\dfrac{(-m^4)^3}{(-m^4)^3}$

$\dfrac{(2m^2)^{-2}}{(2m^2)^{-2}} = \dfrac{-m^{12}}{\frac{1}{4m^4}}$
$= -m^{12} \cdot 4m^4$
$= -4m^{16}$

Exercises

Simplify. Assume that no variable equals 0.

1. $c^{12} \cdot c^{-4} \cdot c^6$ c^{14}

2. $\dfrac{b^8}{b^2}$ b^6

3. $(a^4)^3$ a^{20}

4. $\dfrac{x^{-2}y}{x^4 y^{-1}}$ $\dfrac{y^2}{x^6}$

5. $\left(\dfrac{a^7 b}{a^{-3} b^2}\right)^{-1}$ $\dfrac{b}{a^5}$

6. $\left(\dfrac{x^3 y}{x y^{-2}}\right)^2 \dfrac{x^2}{y^4}$

7. $\frac{1}{2}(-5a^2 b^3)^2(abc)^2$ $5a^6 b^8 c^2$

8. $m^7 \cdot m^8$ m^{15}

9. $\dfrac{8r^{-1}n^2}{4r^2 n^3}$ $\dfrac{2m^2}{n}$

10. $\dfrac{2\frac{3}{4}t^2}{2\frac{2}{4}t^2}$ 2

11. $4j(-j^{-2}k^2)(3j^3 k^{-7}) - \dfrac{12j^2}{k^5}$

12. $\dfrac{2m^2(3m^2 n)^2}{12m^3 n^4}$ $\dfrac{3}{2}m^2$

Chapter 6   5   *Glencoe Algebra 2*

NAME _____ DATE _____ PERIOD _____

6 Anticipation Guide

Polynomials and Polynomial Functions

Step 1   *Before you begin Chapter 6*

- Read each statement.
- Decide whether you Agree (A) or Disagree (D) with the statement.
- Write A or D in the first column OR if you are not sure whether you agree or disagree, write NS (Not Sure).

STEP 1 A, D, or NS	Statement	STEP 2 A or D
	1. The monomial $6m^4 n^2 p^5$ has a degree of 5.	D
	2. To multiply powers of the same variable, add the exponents.	A
	3. $(12t^2 - 3t + 4) - (8t^2 + 4t - 4)$ is equal to $4t^2 - 7t + 8$.	A
	4. $(6x + 2)(7x - 1)$ is equal to $42x^2 - 2$.	D
	5. The *leading coefficient* of a polynomial is the coefficient of the first term.	D
	6. The graph of any polynomial is a parabola.	D
	7. The graph of a polynomial of even degree will approach either $+\infty$ or $-\infty$ as $x \to +\infty$ and as $x \to -\infty$.	A
	8. If the graph of a polynomial function has an x-intercept, then the polynomial has at least one real solution.	A
	9. $a^2 - 2ab - b^2$ is a perfect square trinomial.	D
	10. If $f(a) = 0$, then $x - a$ is a factor of the polynomial $f(x)$.	A
	11. Every polynomial equation with degree greater than 0 has at least one root in the set of complex numbers.	A
	12. To find all the rational zeros of a polynomial function, all the possible zeros must be tested using synthetic substitution.	D

Step 2   *After you complete Chapter 6*

- Reread each statement and complete the last column by entering an A or a D.
- Did any of your opinions about the statements change from the first column?
- For those statements that you mark with a D, use a piece of paper to write an example of why you disagree.

Chapter 6   3   *Glencoe Algebra 2*

Answers (Lesson 6-1)

NAME _____ DATE _____ PERIOD _____

6-1 Skills Practice

Operations with Polynomials

Simplify. Assume that no variable equals 0.

1. $b^4 \cdot b^3$ b^7

2. $c^5 \cdot c^2 \cdot c^2$ c^9

3. $a^{-4} \cdot a^{-3}$ $\dfrac{1}{a^7}$

4. $x^5 \cdot x^{-4} \cdot x \cdot x$ x^2

5. $(2x)^2(4y)^2$ $64x^2y^2$

6. $-2gh(g^3h^6)$ $-2g^4h^6$

7. $10x^3y^8(10x^8)$ $100x^3y^{11}$

8. $\dfrac{24uz^7}{3u^3z^5}$ $\dfrac{8z^2}{w^2}$

9. $\dfrac{-6d^4bc^8}{36a^7b^7c}$ $\dfrac{-c^7}{6a^3b}$

10. $\dfrac{-10pt^4}{-5p^3t^2t}$ $\dfrac{2t^2}{p^2}$

11. $(g + 5) + (2g + 7)$ $3g + 12$

12. $(5d + 5) - (d + 1)$ $4d + 4$

13. $(x^2 - 3x - 3) + (2x^2 + 7x - 2)$ $3x^2 + 4x - 5$

14. $(-2f^2 - 3f - 5) + (-2f^2 - 3f + 8)$ $-4f^2 - 6f + 3$

15. $-5(2z^2 - d^2)$ $-10c^2 + 5d^2$

16. $x^2(2x + 9)$ $2x^3 + 9x^2$

17. $(a - 5)^2$ $a^2 - 10a + 25$

18. $(2x - 3)(3x - 5)$ $6x^2 - 19x + 15$

19. $(r - 2t)(r + 2t)$ $r^2 - 4t^2$

20. $(3y + 4)(2y - 3)$ $6y^2 - y - 12$

21. $(3 - 2b)(3 + 2b)$ $9 - 4b^2$

22. $(3w + 1)^3$ $9w^2 + 6w + 1$

NAME _____ DATE _____ PERIOD _____

6-1 Study Guide and Intervention (continued)

Operations with Polynomials

Operations with Polynomials

| Polynomial | a monomial or a sum of monomials |
| Like Terms | terms that that have the same variable(s) raised to the same power(s) |

To add or subtract polynomials, perform the indicated operations and combine like terms.

Example 1 **Simplify** $4xy^2 + 12xy - 7x^2y - (20xy + 5xy^2 - 8x^2y)$.

$4xy^2 + 12xy - 7x^2y - (20xy + 5xy^2 - 8x^2y)$

$= 4xy^2 + 12xy - 7x^2y - 20xy - 5xy^2 + 8x^2y$ Distribute the minus sign.

$= (-7x^2y + 8x^2y) + (4xy^2 - 5xy^2) + (12xy - 20xy)$ Group like terms.

$= x^2y - xy^2 - 8xy$ Combine like terms.

You use the distributive property when you multiply polynomials. When multiplying binomials, the FOIL pattern is helpful.

| FOIL Pattern | To multiply two binomials, add the products of F the first terms, O the outer terms, I the inner terms, and L the last terms. |

Example 2 **Find** $(6x - 5)(2x + 1)$.

$(6x - 5)(2x + 1) = 6x \cdot 2x + 6x \cdot 1 + (-5) \cdot 2x + (-5) \cdot 1$ First terms Outer terms Inner terms Last terms

$= 12x^2 + 6x - 10x - 5$ Multiply monomials.

$= 12x^2 - 4x - 5$ Add like terms.

Exercises

Simplify.

1. $(6x^2 - 3x + 2) - (4x^2 + x - 3)$ $2x^2 - 4x + 5$

2. $(7y^2 + 12xy - 5x^2) + (6xy - 4y^2 - 3x^2)$ $3y^2 + 18xy - 8x^2$

3. $(-4m^2 - 6m) - (6m + 4m^2)$ $-8m^2 - 12m$

4. $27x^2 - 5y^2 + 12y^2 - 14x^2$ $13x^2 + 7y^2$

5. $\frac{1}{4}x^2 - \frac{3}{8}xy + \frac{1}{2}y^2 - \frac{1}{2}xy + \frac{1}{4}y^2 - \frac{3}{8}x^2$ $-\frac{1}{8}x^2 - \frac{7}{8}xy + \frac{3}{4}y^2$

6. $24p^3 - 15p^2 + 3p - 15p^3 + 13p^2 - 7p$ $9p^3 - 2p^2 - 4p$

Find each product.

7. $2x(3x^2 - 5)$ $6x^3 - 10x$

8. $7a(6 - 2a - a^2)$ $42a - 14a^2 - 7a^3$

9. $(x^2 - 2)(x^2 - 5)$ $x^4 - 7x^2 + 10$

10. $(x + 1)(2x^2 - 3x + 1)$ $2x^3 - x^2 - 2x + 1$

11. $(2n^2 - 3)(n^2 + 5n - 1)$ $2n^4 + 10n^3 - 5n^2 - 15n + 3$

12. $(x - 1)(x^2 - 3x + 4)$ $x^3 - 4x^2 + 7x - 4$

Answers (Lesson 6-1)

NAME _____ DATE _____ PERIOD _____

6-1 Word Problem Practice

Operations with Polynomials

1. THE EARTH Earth's diameter is approximately 1.2756×10^4 kilometers. The surface area of a sphere can be found using the formula $SA = 4\pi r^2$.

1.2756 × 10⁴ km

What is the approximate surface area of Earth?
5.112×10^8 km²

2. VOLUME The volume of a rectangular prism is given by the product of its length, width, and height. Samantha has a rectangular prism that has a length of b^2 units, a width of a units, and a height of $ab + c$ units.

What is the volume of Samantha's rectangular prism? Express your answer in simplified form.
$a^2b^3 + ab^2c$

3. CONSTRUCTION A rectangular deck is built around a square pool. The pool has side length s. The length of the deck is 5 units longer than twice the side length of the pool. The width of the deck is 3 units longer than the side length of the pool. What is the area of the deck in terms of s?
$s^2 + 11s + 15$

4. SAIL BOATS Tamara requests a custom-made sail for her sailboat. The base of her triangular sail is $2x + 1$ and the height is $4x + 6$.

4x + 6
2x + 1

a. Find the area of the sail.
$4x^2 + 8x + 3$

b. If Tamara wants a different fabric on each side of her sail, write a polynomial to represent the total amount of fabric she will need to make the sail.
$8x^2 + 16x + 6$

c. Tamara decides she also wants a special trim for the hypotenuse of her triangular sail. Write an expression that describes the amount of trim she will need.
$\sqrt{20x^2 + 52x + 37}$

Chapter 6   9   Glencoe Algebra 2

NAME _____ DATE _____ PERIOD _____

6-1 Practice

Operations with Polynomials

Simplify. Assume that no variable equals 0.

1. $n^5 \cdot n^2$ **n^7**

2. $y^7 \cdot y^3 \cdot y^2$ **y^{12}**

3. $t^9 \cdot t^{-8}$ **t**

4. $x^{-4} \cdot x^{-4} \cdot x^4$ **$\dfrac{1}{x^4}$**

5. $(2f^4)^6$ **$64f^{24}$**

6. $(-2b^{-2}c^3)^3$ **$-\dfrac{8c^9}{b^6}$**

7. $(4d^2t^2v^{-1})(-5dt^{-3}v^{-1})$ **$-\dfrac{20d^3t^2}{v^5}$**

8. $8u(2z)^3$ **$64uz^3$**

9. $\dfrac{12m^8v^6}{-9my^4}$ **$\dfrac{4m^7y^2}{3}$**

10. $\dfrac{-6s^5x^3}{18sx^7}$ **$-\dfrac{s^4}{3x^4}$**

11. $\dfrac{-27x^3(-x^3)}{16x^4}$ **$\dfrac{27x^6}{16}$**

12. $\left(\dfrac{2}{3r^{-3}s^2z^6}\right)^2$ **$\dfrac{4}{9r^4s^6z^{12}}$**

13. $-(4w^{-3}z^{-5})(8w)^2$ **$-\dfrac{256}{wz^5}$**

14. $(m^4n^6)^4(m^3n^2p^5)^6$ **$m^{34}n^{36}p^{30}$**

15. $\left(\dfrac{3}{2}d^{-1}f^4\right)\left(-\dfrac{4}{3}d^5f^3\right)^3$ **$-12d^{23}f^{19}$**

16. $\left(\dfrac{2x^4y^2}{-x^3y^5}\right)^{-1}$ **$\dfrac{y^6}{4x^2}$**

17. $\dfrac{(3x^{-3}y^3)(5xy^{-8})}{(x^{-3})^3y^{-2}}$ **$\dfrac{15x^{11}}{y^3}$**

18. $\dfrac{-20(m^2v)(-v)^3}{5(-v)^3(-n^4)} - \dfrac{4v^2}{m^2}$ **$-\dfrac{4v^2}{m^2}$**

19. $(3n^2 + 1) + (8n^2 - 8)$ **$11n^2 - 7$**

20. $(6w - 11w^2) - (4 + 7w^2)$ **$-18w^2 + 6w - 4$**

21. $(w + 2t)(w^2 - 2wt + 4t^2)$ **$w^3 + 8t^3$**

22. $(x + y)(x^2 - 3xy + 2y^2)$ **$x^3 - 2x^2y - xy^2 + 2y^3$**

23. **BANKING** Terry invests $1500 in two mutual funds. The first year, one fund grows 3.8% and the other grows 6%. Write a polynomial to represent the amount Terry's $1500 grows to in that year if x represents the amount he invested in the fund with the lesser growth rate. **$-0.022x + 1590$**

24. **GEOMETRY** The area of the base of a rectangular box measures $2x^2 + 4x - 3$ square units. The height of the box measures x units. Find a polynomial expression for the volume of the box. **$2x^3 + 4x^2 - 3x$ units³**

Chapter 6   8   Glencoe Algebra 2

Chapter 6   **A3**   *Glencoe Algebra 2*

Answers (Lesson 6-1 and Lesson 6-2)

NAME _____ DATE _____ PERIOD _____

6-2 Study Guide and Intervention

Dividing Polynomials

Long Division To divide a polynomial by a monomial, use the skills learned in Lesson 6-1.

To divide a polynomial by a polynomial, use a long division pattern. Remember that only like terms can be added or subtracted.

Example 1 Simplify $\dfrac{12p^3t^2r - 21p^2qtr^2 - 9p^3tr}{3p^4tr}$.

$$\dfrac{12p^3t^2r - 21p^2qtr^2 - 9p^3tr}{3p^4tr} = \dfrac{12p^3t^2r}{3p^4tr} - \dfrac{21p^2qtr^2}{3p^4tr} - \dfrac{9p^3tr}{3p^4tr}$$

$$= \dfrac{12}{3}p^{(3-2)}t^{(2-1)}r^{(1-1)} - \dfrac{21}{3}p^{(2-2)}qt^{(1-1)}r^{(2-1)} - \dfrac{9}{3}p^{(3-2)}t^{(1-1)}r^{(1-1)}$$

$$= 4pt - 7qr - 3p$$

Example 2 Use long division to find $(x^3 - 8x^2 + 4x - 9) \div (x - 4)$.

$$
\begin{array}{r}
x^2 - 4x - 12 \\
x - 4 \overline{)\, x^3 - 8x^2 + 4x - 9} \\
(-)\, \underline{x^3 - 4x^2} \\
-4x^2 + 4x \\
(-)\, \underline{-4x^2 + 16x} \\
-12x - 9 \\
(-)\, \underline{-12x + 48} \\
-57
\end{array}
$$

The quotient is $x^2 - 4x - 12$, and the remainder is -57.

Therefore $\dfrac{x^3 - 8x^2 - 4x - 9}{x - 4} = x^2 - 4x - 12 - \dfrac{57}{x - 4}$.

Exercises

Simplify.

1. $\dfrac{18a^3 + 30a^2}{3a}$

   $6a^2 + 10a$

2. $\dfrac{24mn^6 - 40m^2n^3}{4m^2n^3}$

   $\dfrac{6n^3}{m} - 10$

3. $\dfrac{60a^2b^3 - 48b^7 + 84a^5b^2}{12ab^2}$

   $5ab - \dfrac{4b^2}{a} + 7a^4$

4. $(2x^2 - 5x - 3) \div (x - 3)$

   $2x + 1$

5. $(m^2 - 3m - 7) \div (m + 2)$

   $m - 5 + \dfrac{3}{m + 2}$

6. $(p^3 - 6) \div (p - 1)$

   $p^2 + p + 1 - \dfrac{5}{p - 1}$

7. $(t^3 - 6t^2 + 1) \div (t + 2)$

   $t^2 - 8t + 16 - \dfrac{31}{t + 2}$

8. $(x^5 - 1) \div (x - 1)$

   $x^4 + x^3 + x^2 + x + 1$

9. $(2x^3 - 5x^2 + 4x - 4) \div (x - 2)$

   $2x^2 - x + 2$

NAME _____ DATE _____ PERIOD _____

6-1 Enrichment

Polynomials with Fractional Coefficients

Polynomials may have fractional coefficients as long as there are no variables in the denominators. Computing with fractional coefficients is performed in the same way as computing with whole-number coefficients.

Simplify. Write all coefficients as fractions.

1. $\left(\dfrac{3}{5}m - \dfrac{2}{7}p - \dfrac{1}{3}n\right) - \left(\dfrac{7}{3}p - \dfrac{5}{2}m - \dfrac{3}{4}n\right)$

   $\dfrac{31}{10}m + \dfrac{5}{12}n - \dfrac{55}{21}p$

2. $\left(\dfrac{3}{2}x - \dfrac{4}{3}y - \dfrac{5}{4}z\right) + \left(\dfrac{1}{4}x + y + \dfrac{2}{5}z\right) + \left(-\dfrac{7}{8}x - \dfrac{6}{7}y + \dfrac{1}{2}z\right)$

   $\dfrac{3}{8}x - \dfrac{25}{21}y - \dfrac{7}{20}z$

3. $\left(\dfrac{1}{2}a^2 - \dfrac{1}{3}ab + \dfrac{1}{4}b^2\right) + \left(\dfrac{5}{6}a^2 + \dfrac{2}{3}ab - \dfrac{3}{4}b^2\right)$

   $\dfrac{4}{3}a^2 + \dfrac{1}{3}ab - \dfrac{1}{2}b^2$

4. $\left(\dfrac{1}{2}a^2 - \dfrac{1}{3}ab + \dfrac{1}{4}b^2\right) - \left(\dfrac{1}{3}a^2 - \dfrac{1}{2}ab + \dfrac{5}{6}b^2\right)$

   $\dfrac{1}{6}a^2 + \dfrac{1}{6}ab - \dfrac{7}{12}b^2$

5. $\left(\dfrac{1}{2}a^2 - \dfrac{1}{3}ab + \dfrac{1}{4}b^2\right) \cdot \left(\dfrac{1}{2}a - \dfrac{2}{3}b\right)$

   $\dfrac{1}{4}a^3 - \dfrac{1}{2}a^2b + \dfrac{25}{72}ab^2 - \dfrac{1}{6}b^3$

6. $\left(\dfrac{2}{3}a^2 - \dfrac{1}{5}a + \dfrac{2}{7}\right) \cdot \left(\dfrac{2}{3}a^3 + \dfrac{1}{5}a^2 - \dfrac{2}{7}a\right)$

   $\dfrac{4}{9}a^5 - \dfrac{1}{25}a^3 + \dfrac{4}{35}a^2 - \dfrac{4}{49}a$

7. $\left(\dfrac{2}{3}x^3 - \dfrac{3}{4}x - 2\right) \cdot \left(\dfrac{4}{5}x - \dfrac{1}{2}x^2 - \dfrac{1}{2}\right)$

   $-\dfrac{1}{9}x^4 + \dfrac{79}{120}x^3 - \dfrac{3}{5}x^2 - \dfrac{49}{40}x + 1$

8. $\left(\dfrac{1}{6} + \dfrac{1}{3}x + \dfrac{1}{6}x^4 - \dfrac{1}{2}x^2\right) \cdot \left(\dfrac{1}{6}x^3 - 1 - \dfrac{1}{3}x\right)$

   $\dfrac{1}{36}x^7 - \dfrac{5}{36}x^5 + \dfrac{7}{36}x^3 + \dfrac{1}{18}x^2 - \dfrac{1}{6}x - \dfrac{1}{18}$

NAME _____ DATE _____ PERIOD _____

6-2 Skills Practice

Dividing Polynomials

Simplify.

1. $\dfrac{10c+6}{2}$ **5c + 3**

2. $\dfrac{12x+20}{4}$ **3x + 5**

3. $\dfrac{15y^3+6y^2+3y}{3y}$ **5y² + 2y + 1**

4. $\dfrac{12x^3-4x-8}{4x}$ **3x − 1 − $\dfrac{2}{x}$**

5. $(15q^6 + 5q^2)(5q)^{-1}$ **3q² + $\dfrac{1}{q^2}$**

6. $(4f^5 - 6f^4 + 12f^3 - 8f^2)(4f^2)^{-1}$ **f³ − $\dfrac{3f^2}{2}$ + 3f − 2**

7. $(6j^2k - 9jk^3) \div 3jk$ **2j − 3k**

8. $(4a^3h^2 - 8a^2h + 3a^4) \div (2a^2)$ **2h² − 4ah + $\dfrac{3a^2}{2}$**

9. $(n^2 + 7n + 10) \div (n + 5)$ **n + 2**

10. $(d^2 + 4d + 3) \div (d + 1)$ **d + 3**

11. $(2t^2 + 13t + 15) \div (t + 5)$ **2t + 3**

12. $(6y^2 + y - 2)(2y - 1)^{-1}$ **3y + 2**

13. $(4g^2 - 9) \div (2g + 3)$ **2g − 3**

14. $(2x^2 - 5x - 4) \div (x - 3)$ **2x + 1 − $\dfrac{1}{x-3}$**

15. $\dfrac{u^2+5u-12}{u-3}$ **u + 8 + $\dfrac{12}{u-3}$**

16. $\dfrac{2x^2-5x-4}{x-3}$ **2x + 1 − $\dfrac{1}{x-3}$**

17. $(3v^2 - 7v - 10)(v - 4)^{-1}$ **3v + 5 + $\dfrac{10}{v-4}$**

18. $(3t^4 + 4t^3 - 32t^2 - 5t - 20)(t + 4)^{-1}$ **3t³ − 8t² − 5**

19. $\dfrac{y^3-y^2-6}{y+2}$ **y² − 3y + 6 − $\dfrac{18}{y+2}$**

20. $\dfrac{2x^3-x^2-19x+15}{x-3}$ **2x² + 5x − 4 + $\dfrac{3}{x-3}$**

21. $(4p^3 - 3p^2 + 2p) \div (p - 1)$ **4p² + p + 3 + $\dfrac{3}{p-1}$**

22. $(3c^4 + 6c^3 - 2c + 4)(c + 2)^{-1}$ **3c³ − 2 + $\dfrac{8}{c-2}$**

23. **GEOMETRY** The area of a rectangle is $x^3 + 8x^2 + 13x - 12$ square units. The width of the rectangle is $x + 4$ units. What is the length of the rectangle? **x² + 4x − 3 units**

NAME _____ DATE _____ PERIOD _____

6-2 Study Guide and Intervention (continued)

Dividing Polynomials

Synthetic Division

Synthetic division	a procedure to divide a polynomial by a binomial using coefficients of the dividend and the value of r in the divisor x − r

Use synthetic division to find $(2x^3 - 5x^2 + 5x - 2) \div (x - 1)$.

Step 1	Write the terms of the dividend so that the degrees of the terms are in descending order. Then write just the coefficients.	2x³ − 5x² + 5x − 2 → 2 −5 5 −2
Step 2	Write the constant r of the divisor x − r to the left. In this case, r = 1. Bring down the first coefficient, 2, as shown.	1| 2 −5 5 −2 2
Step 3	Multiply the first coefficient by r, 1·2=2. Write their product under the second coefficient. Then add the product and the second coefficient: −5 + 2 = −3.	1| 2 −5 5 −2 ↓ 2 2 −3
Step 4	Multiply the sum, −3, by r: −3·1 = −3. Write the product under the next coefficient and add: 5 + (−3) = 2.	1| 2 −5 5 −2 ↓ 2 −3 2 −3 2
Step 5	Multiply the sum, 2, by r: 2·1 = 2. Write the product under the next coefficient and add: −2 + 2 = 0. The remainder is 0.	1| 2 −5 5 −2 ↓ 2 −3 2 2 −3 2 0

Thus, $(2x^3 - 5x^2 + 5x - 2) \div (x - 1) = 2x^2 - 3x + 2$.

Exercises

Simplify.

1. $(3x^3 - 7x^2 + 9x - 14) \div (x - 2)$ **3x² − x + 7**

2. $(5x^3 + 7x^2 - x - 3) \div (x + 1)$ **5x² + 2x − 3**

3. $(2x^3 + 3x^2 - 10x - 3) \div (x + 3)$ **2x² − 3x − 1**

4. $(x^3 - 8x^2 + 19x - 9) \div (x - 1)$ **x² − 4x + 3 + $\dfrac{3}{x-4}$**

5. $(2x^3 + 10x^2 + 9x + 38) \div (x + 5)$ **2x² + 9 − $\dfrac{7}{x+5}$**

6. $(3x^3 - 8x^2 + 16x - 1) \div (x - 1)$ **3x² − 5x + 11 + $\dfrac{10}{x-1}$**

7. $(x^3 - 9x^2 + 17x - 1) \div (x - 2)$ **x² − 7x + 3 + $\dfrac{5}{x-2}$**

8. $(4x^3 - 25x^2 + 4x + 20) \div (x - 6)$ **4x² − x − 2 + $\dfrac{8}{x-6}$**

9. $(6x^3 + 28x^2 - 7x + 9) \div (x + 5)$ **6x² − 2x + 3 − $\dfrac{6}{x+5}$**

10. $(x^4 - 4x^3 + x^2 + 7x - 2) \div (x - 2)$ **x³ − 2x² − 3x + 1**

11. $(12x^4 + 20x^3 - 24x^2 + 20x + 35) \div (3x + 5)$ **4x³ − 8x + 20 − $\dfrac{65}{3x+5}$**

6-2 Practice

Dividing Polynomials

Simplify.

1. $\dfrac{15r^{10} - 5r^8 + 40r^2}{5r^4}$ $3r^6 - r^4 + \dfrac{8}{r^2}$

2. $\dfrac{6k^3m - 12k^3m^2 + 9m^3}{2bm^2}$ $-6k^2 + \dfrac{9m}{2k}$

3. $(-30x^3y + 12x^2y^2 - 18x^2y) \div (-6x^2y)$ $5x - 2y + 3$

4. $(-6w^3z^4 - 3w^2z^5 + 4w + 5z) \div (2w^2z)$ $-3wz^3 - \dfrac{3z^4}{2} + \dfrac{2}{wz} + \dfrac{5}{2w^2}$

5. $(4a^3 - 8a^2 + a^3)(4a)^{-1}$ $a^2 - 2a + \dfrac{a}{4}$

6. $(28d^{13}k^2 + d^2k^2 - 4dk^2)(4dk^2)^{-1}$ $7d^2 + \dfrac{d}{4} - 1$

7. $\dfrac{f^3 + 7f + 10}{f + 2}$ $f + 5$

8. $\dfrac{2x^2 + 3x - 14}{x - 2}$ $2x + 7$

9. $(a^3 - 64) \div (a - 4)$ $a^2 + 4a + 16$

10. $(b^3 + 27) \div (b + 3)$ $b^2 - 3b + 9$

11. $\dfrac{2x^3 + 6x + 152}{x + 4}$ $2x^2 - 8x + 38$

12. $\dfrac{2x^3 + 4x - 6}{x + 3}$ $2x^2 - 6x + 22 - \dfrac{72}{x + 3}$

13. $(3u^3 + 7w^2 - 4w + 3) \div (w + 3)$ $3w^2 - 2w + 2 - \dfrac{3}{w + 3}$

14. $(6y^4 + 15y^3 - 28y - 6) \div (y + 2)$ $6y^3 + 3y^2 - 6y - 16 + \dfrac{26}{y + 2}$

15. $(x^4 - 3x^3 - 11x^2 + 3x + 10) \div (x - 5)$ $x^3 + 2x^2 - x - 2$

16. $(3m^5 + m - 1) \div (m + 1)$ $3m^4 - 3m^3 + 3m^2 - 3m + 4 - \dfrac{5}{m + 1}$

17. $(x^4 - 3x^3 + 5x - 6)(x + 2)^{-1}$ $x^3 - 5x^2 + 10x - 15 + \dfrac{24}{x + 2}$

18. $(6y^2 - 5y - 15)(2y + 3)^{-1}$ $3y - 7 + \dfrac{6}{2y + 3}$

19. $\dfrac{4x^2 - 2x + 6}{2x - 3}$ $2x + 2 + \dfrac{12}{2x - 3}$

20. $\dfrac{6x^2 - x - 7}{3x + 1}$ $2x - 1 - \dfrac{6}{3x + 1}$

21. $(2r^3 + 5r^2 - 2r - 15) \div (2r - 3)$ $r^2 + 4r + 5$

22. $(6t^3 + 5t^2 - 2t + 1) \div (3t + 1)$ $2t^2 + t - 1 + \dfrac{2}{3t + 1}$

23. $\dfrac{4p^4 - 17p^2 + 14p - 3}{2p - 3}$ $2p^3 + 3p^2 - 4p + 1$

24. $\dfrac{2h^4 - h^3 + h^2 + h - 3}{h^2 - 1}$ $2h^2 - h + 3$

25. **GEOMETRY** The area of a rectangle is $2x^2 - 11x + 15$ square feet. The length of the rectangle is $2x - 5$ feet. What is the width of the rectangle? $x - 3$ ft

26. **GEOMETRY** The area of a triangle is $15x^4 + 3x^3 + 4x^2 - x - 3$ square meters. The length of the base of the triangle is $6x^2 - 2$ meters. What is the height of the triangle? $5x^2 + x + 3$ m

---

6-2 Word Problem Practice

Dividing Polynomials

1. **REMAINDERS** Jordan divided the polynomial $x^4 + x - 6$ into the polynomial $p(x)$ yesterday. Today his work is smudged and he cannot read $p(x)$ or most of his answer. The only part he could read was the remainder $x + 4$. His teacher wants him to find $p(-3)$. What is $p(-3)$?
1

2. **LONG DIVISION** Dana used long division to divide $x^4 + x^3 + x^2 + x + 1$ by $x + 2$. Her work is shown below with three numbers missing.

$$\begin{array}{r}
x^3 - x^2 + 3x - 5 \\
\hline
x + 2\,)\,x^4 + x^3 + x^2 + x + 1 \\
(-)\,x^4 + 2x^3 \\
\hline
-x^3 + A \\
(-)\,-x^3 + 2x^2 \\
\hline
3x^2 + x \\
(-)\,3x^2 + B \\
\hline
-5x + 1 \\
(-)\,-5x - 10 \\
\hline
C
\end{array}$$

What are A, B, and C?
A is x^2; B is $6x$; C is 11.

3. **AVERAGES** Shelby is a statistician. She has a list of $n + 1$ numbers and she needs to find their average. Two of the numbers are n^3 and 2. Each of the other $n - 1$ numbers are all equal to 1. What is the average of these numbers?
$n^2 - n + 2 - \dfrac{1}{n + 1}$

4. **VOLUME** The volume of one column of the Lincoln Memorial is $\pi(x^3 - 32x^2 - 224x + 640)$. If the height of the column is $x + 40$ feet, find the area of the base of the column in terms of x and π.
$\pi(x^2 - 8x + 16)$

5. **NUMBER THEORY** Mr. Collins has his class working with bases and polynomials. He wrote on the board that the number 1111 in base B has the value $B^3 + B^2 + B + 1$. The class was then given the following questions to answer.

a. The number 11 in base B has the value $B + 1$. What is 1111 (in base B) divided by 11 (in base B)?
$B^2 + 1$

b. The number 111 in base B has the value $B^2 + B + 1$. What is 1111 (in base B) divided by 111 (in base B)?
$B + \dfrac{1}{B^2 + B + 1}$

Answers (Lesson 6-2 and Lesson 6-3)

6-2 Enrichment

Oblique Asymptotes

The graph of $y = ax + b$, where $a \neq 0$, is called an oblique asymptote of $y = f(x)$ if the graph of f comes closer and closer to the line as $x \to \infty$ or $x \to -\infty$. ∞ is the mathematical symbol for infinity, which means *endless*.

For $f(x) = 3x + 4 + \frac{2}{x}$, $y = 3x + 4$ is an oblique asymptote because $f(x) - 3x - 4 = \frac{2}{x}$, and $\frac{2}{x} \to 0$ as $x \to \infty$ or $\to -\infty$. In other words, as $|x|$ increases, the value of $\frac{2}{x}$ gets smaller and smaller approaching 0.

Example Find the oblique asymptote for $f(x) = \dfrac{x^2 + 8x + 15}{x + 2}$.

$$\begin{array}{r|rrr} -2 & 1 & 8 & 15 \\ & & -2 & -12 \\ \hline & 1 & 6 & 3 \end{array}$$ Use synthetic division.

$y = \dfrac{x^2 - 8x + 15}{x + 2} = x + 6 + \dfrac{3}{x+2}$

As $|x|$ increases, the value of $\dfrac{3}{x+2}$ gets smaller. In other words, since $\dfrac{3}{x+2} \to 0$ as $x \to \infty$ or $x \to -\infty$, $y = x + 6$ is an oblique asymptote.

Exercises

Use synthetic division to find the oblique asymptote for each function.

1. $y = \dfrac{8x^2 - 4x + 11}{x + 5}$ $y = 8x - 44$

2. $y = \dfrac{x^2 + 3x - 15}{x - 2}$ $y = x + 5$

3. $y = \dfrac{x^2 - 2x - 18}{x - 3}$ $y = x + 1$

4. $y = \dfrac{ax^2 + bx + c}{x - d}$ $y = ax + b + ad$

5. $y = \dfrac{ax^2 + bx + c}{x + d}$ $y = ax + b - ad$

Chapter 6   16   Glencoe Algebra 2

6-3 Study Guide and Intervention

Polynomial Functions

Polynomial Functions

Polynomial in One Variable	A polynomial of degree n in one variable x is an expression of the form $a_n x^n + a_{n-1} x^{n-1} + \cdots + a_2 x^2 + a_1 x + a_0$, where the coefficients $a_{n-1}, a_{n-2}, a_{n-3}, \ldots, a_0$ represent real numbers, a_n is not zero, and n represents a nonnegative integer.

The **degree** of a polynomial in one variable is the greatest exponent of its variable. The **leading coefficient** is the coefficient of the term with the highest degree.

Polynomial Function	A polynomial function of degree n can be described by an equation of the form $P(x) = a_n x^n + a_{n-1} x^{n-1} + \cdots + a_2 x^2 + a_1 x + a_0$, where the coefficients $a_{n-1}, a_{n-2}, a_{n-3}, \ldots, a_0$ represent real numbers, a_n is not zero, and n represents a nonnegative integer.

Example 1 What are the degree and leading coefficient of $3x^2 - 2x^4 - 7 + x^3$?

Rewrite the expression so the powers of x are in decreasing order.

$-2x^4 + x^3 + 3x^2 - 7$

This is a polynomial in one variable. The degree is 4, and the leading coefficient is -2.

Example 2 Find $f(-5)$ if $f(x) = x^3 + 2x^2 - 10x + 20$.

$f(x) = x^3 + 2x^2 - 10x + 20$ Original function
$f(-5) = (-5)^3 + 2(-5)^2 - 10(-5) + 20$ Replace x with -5.
$= -125 + 50 + 50 + 20$ Evaluate.
$= -5$ Simplify.

Example 3 Find $g(a^2 - 1)$ if $g(x) = x^2 + 3x - 4$.

$g(x) = x^2 + 3x - 4$ Original function
$g(a^2 - 1) = (a^2 - 1)^2 + 3(a^2 - 1) - 4$ Replace x with $a^2 - 1$.
$= a^4 - 2a^2 + 1 + 3a^2 - 3 - 4$ Evaluate.
$= a^4 + a^2 - 6$ Simplify.

Exercises

State the degree and leading coefficient of each polynomial in one variable. If it is not a polynomial in one variable, explain why.

1. $3x^4 + 6x^3 - x^2 + 12$ **4; 3**

2. $100 - 5x^3 + 10x^7$ **7; 10**

3. $4x^6 + 6x^4 + 8x^3 - 10x^2 + 20$ **8; 8**

4. $4x^2 - 3xy + 16y^2$ **not a polynomial in one variable; contains two variables**

5. $8x^3 - 9x^5 + 4x^2 - 36$ **5; −9**

6. $\dfrac{x^2}{18} - \dfrac{x^6}{25} + \dfrac{x^3}{36} - \dfrac{1}{72}$ **6; $-\dfrac{1}{25}$**

Find $f(2)$ and $f(-5)$ for each function.

7. $f(x) = x^2 - 9$ **−5; 16**

8. $f(x) = 4x^3 - 3x^2 + 2x - 1$ **23; −586**

9. $f(x) = 9x^3 - 4x^2 + 5x + 7$ **73; −1243**

Chapter 6   17   Glencoe Algebra 2

NAME _____ DATE _____ PERIOD _____

6-3 Skills Practice

Polynomial Functions

State the degree and leading coefficient of each polynomial in one variable. If it is not a polynomial in one variable, explain why.

1. $a + 8$ **1; 1**

2. $(2x - 1)(4x^2 + 3)$ **3; 8**

3. $-5x^5 + 3x^3 - 8$ **5; -5**

4. $18 - 3y + 5y^2 - y^5 + 7y^6$ **6; 7**

5. $u^3 + 4u^2t^2 + t^4$ **No, this polynomial contains two variables, u and t.**

6. $2r - r^2 + \dfrac{1}{r^2}$ **No, this is not a polynomial because $\dfrac{1}{r^2}$ cannot be written in the form r^n, where n is a nonnegative integer.**

Find $p(-1)$ and $p(2)$ for each function.

7. $p(x) = 4 - 3x$ **7; -2**

8. $p(x) = 3x + x^2$ **-2; 10**

9. $p(x) = 2x^2 - 4x + 1$ **7; 1**

10. $p(x) = -2x^3 + 5x + 3$ **0; -3**

11. $p(x) = x^4 + 8x^2 - 10$ **-1; 38**

12. $p(x) = \dfrac{1}{3}x^2 - \dfrac{2}{3}x + 2$ **3; 2**

If $p(x) = 4x^2 - 3$ and $r(x) = 1 + 3x$, find each value.

13. $p(a)$ **$4a^2 - 3$**

14. $r(2a)$ **$1 + 6a$**

15. $3r(a)$ **$3 + 9a$**

16. $-4p(a)$ **$-16a^2 + 12$**

17. $p(a^2)$ **$4a^4 - 3$**

18. $r(x + 2)$ **$7 + 3x$**

For each graph,
a. describe the end behavior,
b. determine whether it represents an odd-degree or an even-degree function, and
c. state the number of real zeroes.

19.

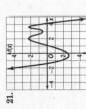

$f(x) \to +\infty$ as $x \to +\infty$, $f(x) \to -\infty$ as $x \to -\infty$;
odd; 1

20.

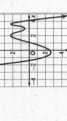

$f(x) \to -\infty$ as $x \to +\infty$, $f(x) \to -\infty$ as $x \to -\infty$;
even; 4

21.

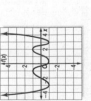

$f(x) \to -\infty$ as $x \to +\infty$, $f(x) \to +\infty$ as $x \to -\infty$;
odd; 3

Chapter 6   19   Glencoe Algebra 2

NAME _____ DATE _____ PERIOD _____

6-3 Study Guide and Intervention (continued)

Polynomial Functions

Graphs of Polynomial Functions

End Behavior of Polynomial Functions	If the degree is even and the leading coefficient is positive, then
	$f(x) \to +\infty$ as $x \to -\infty$ $f(x) \to +\infty$ as $x \to +\infty$
	If the degree is even and the leading coefficient is negative, then
	$f(x) \to -\infty$ as $x \to -\infty$ $f(x) \to -\infty$ as $x \to +\infty$
	If the degree is odd and the leading coefficient is positive, then
	$f(x) \to -\infty$ as $x \to -\infty$ $f(x) \to +\infty$ as $x \to +\infty$
	If the degree is odd and the leading coefficient is negative, then
	$f(x) \to +\infty$ as $x \to -\infty$ $f(x) \to -\infty$ as $x \to +\infty$

Real Zeros of a Polynomial Function	The maximum number of zeros of a polynomial function is equal to the degree of the polynomial. A zero of a function is a point at which the graph intersects the x-axis. On a graph, count the number of real zeros of the function by counting the number of times the graph crosses or touches the x-axis.

Example   Determine whether the graph represents an odd-degree polynomial or an even-degree polynomial. Then state the number of real zeros.

As $x \to -\infty$, $f(x) \to -\infty$ and as $x \to +\infty$, $f(x) \to +\infty$, so it is an odd-degree polynomial function.
The graph intersects the x-axis at 1 point, so the function has 1 real zero.

Exercises

For each graph,
a. describe the end behavior,
b. determine whether it represents an odd-degree or an even-degree function, and
c. state the number of real zeroes.

1.

even; 6

2.

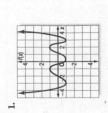

even; 1 double zero

3.

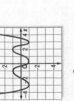

odd; 3

Chapter 6   18   Glencoe Algebra 2

Chapter 6   A8   Glencoe Algebra 2

NAME _____ DATE _____ PERIOD _____

6-3 Practice

Polynomial Functions

State the degree and leading coefficient of each polynomial in one variable. If it is not a polynomial in one variable, explain why.

1. $(3x^2 + 1)(2x^2 - 9)$ 4; 6

2. $\frac{1}{5}a^3 - \frac{3}{5}a^2 + \frac{4}{5}a$ 3; $\frac{1}{5}$

3. $\frac{2}{m^2} + 3m - 12$ Not a polynomial; $\frac{2}{m^2}$ cannot be written in the form m^n for a nonnegative integer n.

4. $27 + 3xy^3 - 12x^2y^2 - 10y$ No, this polynomial contains two variables, x and y.

Find $p(-2)$ and $p(3)$ for each function.

5. $p(x) = x^3 - x^5$
24; −216

6. $p(x) = -7x^2 + 5x + 9$
−29; −39

7. $p(x) = -x^5 + 4x^3$
0; −135

8. $p(x) = 3x^3 - x^2 + 2x - 5$
−37; 73

9. $p(x) = x^4 + \frac{1}{2}x^3 - \frac{1}{2}x$
13; 93

10. $p(x) = \frac{1}{3x^3} + \frac{2}{3x^2} + 3x$
−6; 24

If $p(x) = 3x^2 - 4$ and $r(x) = 2x^2 - 5x + 1$, find each value.

11. $p(8a)$
192a² − 4

12. $r(a^2)$
2a⁴ − 5a² + 1

13. $-5r(2a)$
−40a² + 50a − 5

14. $r(x + 2)$
2x² + 3x − 1

15. $p(x^2 - 1)$
3x⁴ − 6x² − 1

16. $5p(x + 2)$
15x² + 60x + 40

For each graph,
a. describe the end behavior,
b. determine whether it represents an odd-degree or an even-degree function, and
c. state the number of real zeroes.

17.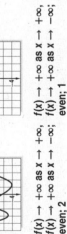
$f(x) \to +\infty$ as $x \to +\infty$;
$f(x) \to +\infty$ as $x \to -\infty$;
even; 2

18.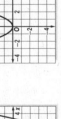
$f(x) \to +\infty$ as $x \to +\infty$, $f(x) \to -\infty$ as $x \to -\infty$;
odd; 1

19.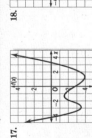
$f(x) \to -\infty$ as $x \to +\infty$, $f(x) \to -\infty$ as $x \to -\infty$;
even; 5

20. WIND CHILL The function $C(w) = 0.013w^2 - w - 7$ estimates the wind chill temperature $C(w)$ at 0°F for wind speeds w from 5 to 30 miles per hour. Estimate the wind chill temperature at 0°F if the wind speed is 20 miles per hour. about −22°F

NAME _____ DATE _____ PERIOD _____

6-3 Word Problem Practice

Polynomial Functions

1. MANUFACTURING A metal sheet is curved according to the shape of the graph of $f(x) = x^4 - 9x^2$. What is the degree of this polynomial?
4

2. GRAPHS Kendra graphed the polynomial $f(x)$ shown below.

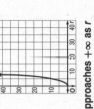

From this graph, describe the end behavior, degree, and sign of the leading coefficient.

$f(x) \to -\infty$ as $x \to +\infty$ and
$f(x) \to +\infty$ as $x \to -\infty$; the
degree is 3; the leading
coefficient is negative

3. PENTAGONAL NUMBERS The nth pentagonal number is given by the expression

$$\frac{n(3n - 1)}{2}$$

What is the degree of this polynomial? What is the seventh pentagonal number?
2; 70

4. DRILLING The volume of a drill bit can be estimated by the formula for a cone, $V = \frac{1}{3}\pi h r^2$, where h is the height of the bit and r is its radius. Substituting $\frac{\sqrt{3}}{3}r$ for h, the volume of the drill bit is estimated as $\frac{\sqrt{3}}{9}\pi r^3$. Graph the function of drill bit volume. Describe the end behavior, degree, and sign of the leading coefficient.

V approaches +∞ as r
approaches +∞; degree = 3; sign
of the leading coefficient is
positive

5. TRIANGLES Dylan drew n dots on a piece of paper making sure that no line contained 3 of the dots. The number of triangles that can be made using the dots as vertices is equal to
$f(n) = \frac{1}{6}(n^3 - 3n^2 + 2n)$.

a. What is the degree of f?
3

b. If Dylan drew 15 dots, how many triangles can be made?
455

Answers (Lesson 6-3 and Lesson 6-4)

6-4 Study Guide and Intervention

Analyzing Graphs of Polynomial Functions

Graphs of Polynomial Functions

Location Principle	Suppose $y = f(x)$ represents a polynomial function and a and b are two numbers such that $f(a) < 0$ and $f(b) > 0$. Then the function has at least one real zero between a and b.

Example **Determine consecutive integer values of x between which each real zero of $f(x) = 2x^4 - x^3 - 5$ is located. Then draw the graph.**

Make a table of values. Look at the values of $f(x)$ to locate the zeros. Then use the points to sketch a graph of the function.

x	$f(x)$
-2	35
-1	-2
0	-5
1	-4
2	19

The changes in sign indicate that there are zeros between $x = -2$ and $x = -1$ and between $x = 1$ and $x = 2$.

Exercises

Graph each function by making a table of values. Determine the values of x between which each real zero is located.

1. $f(x) = x^3 - 2x^2 + 1$

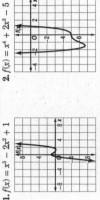

between 0 and -1;
at 1; between 1 and 2

2. $f(x) = x^4 + 2x^3 - 5$

between -2 and -3;
between 1 and 2

3. $f(x) = -x^4 + 2x^2 - 1$

at ±1

4. $f(x) = x^3 - 3x^2 + 4$

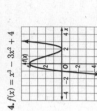

at -1, 2

5. $f(x) = 3x^3 + 2x - 1$

between 0 and 1

6. $f(x) = x^4 - 3x^3 + 1$

between 0 and 1;
between 2 and 3

6-3 Enrichment

Approximation by Means of Polynomials

Many scientific experiments produce pairs of numbers $[x, f(x)]$ that can be related by a formula. If the pairs form a function, you can fit a polynomial to the pairs in exactly one way. Consider the pairs given by the following table.

x	1	2	4	7
$f(x)$	6	11	39	-54

We will assume the polynomial is of degree three. Substitute the given values into this expression.

$$f(x) = A + B(x - x_0) + C(x - x_0)(x - x_1) + D(x - x_0)(x - x_1)(x - x_2)$$

You will get the system of equations shown below. You can solve this system and use the values for A, B, C, and D to find the desired polynomial.

$6 = A$
$11 = A + B(2 - 1) = A + B$
$39 = A + B(4 - 1) + C(4 - 1)(4 - 2) = A + 3B + 6C$
$-54 = A + B(7 - 1) + C(7 - 1)(7 - 2) + D(7 - 1)(7 - 2)(7 - 4) = A + 6B + 30C + 90D$

Solve.

1. Solve the system of equations for the values A, B, C, and D.

   $A = 6, B = 5, C = 3, D = -2$

2. Find the polynomial that represents the four ordered pairs. Write your answer in the form $y = a + bx + cx^2 + dx^3$.

   $y = -2x^3 + 17x^2 - 32x + 23$

3. Find the polynomial that gives the following values.

x	8	12	15	20
$f(x)$	-207	169	976	3801

   $A = -207, B = 94, C = 25, D = 1; y = x^3 - 10x^2 - 10x + 1$

4. A scientist measured the volume $f(x)$ of carbon dioxide gas that can be absorbed by one cubic centimeter of charcoal at pressure x. Find the values for A, B, C, and D.

x	120	340	534	698
$f(x)$	3.1	5.5	7.1	8.3

   $A = 3.1, B = 0.01091, C = -0.00000643, D = 0.0000000066$

NAME _____ DATE _____ PERIOD _____

6-4 Skills Practice

Analyzing Graphs of Polynomial Functions

Complete each of the following,
a. Graph each function by making a table of values.
b. Determine the consecutive values of x between which each real zero is located.
c. Estimate the x-coordinates at which the relative maxima and minima occur.

1. $f(x) = x^3 - 3x^2 + 1$

x	f(x)
-2	-19
-1	-3
0	1
1	-1
2	-3
3	1
4	17

zeros between −1 and 0, 0 and 1, and 2 and 3; rel. max. at x = 0, rel. min. at x = 2

2. $f(x) = x^3 - 3x + 1$

x	f(x)
-3	-17
-2	1
-1	3
0	1
1	-1
2	3
3	19

zeros between −2 and −1, 0 and 1, and 1 and 2; rel. max. at x = −1, rel. min. at x = 1

3. $f(x) = 2x^3 + 9x^2 + 12x + 2$

x	f(x)
-3	-7
-2	-2
-1	-3
0	2
1	25

zero between −1 and 0; rel. max. at x = −2, rel. min. at x = −1

4. $f(x) = 2x^3 - 3x^2 + 2$

x	f(x)
-1	-3
0	2
1	1
2	6
3	29

zero between −1 and 0; rel. max. at x = 0, rel. min. at x = 1

5. $f(x) = x^4 - 2x^2 - 2$

x	f(x)
-3	61
-2	6
-1	-3
0	-2
1	-3
2	6
3	61

zeros between −2 and −1, and 1 and 2; rel. max. at x = 0, rel. min. at x = −1 and x = 1

6. $f(x) = 0.5x^4 - 4x^2 + 4$

x	f(x)
-3	8.5
-2	-4
-1	0.5
0	4
1	0.5
2	-4
3	8.5

zeros between −1 and −2, −2 and −3, 1 and 2, and 2 and 3; rel. max. at rel. x = 0, rel. min. at x = −2 and x = 2

NAME _____ DATE _____ PERIOD _____

6-4 Study Guide and Intervention (continued)

Analyzing Graphs of Polynomial Functions

Maximum and Minimum Points A quadratic function has either a maximum or a minimum point on its graph. For higher degree polynomial functions, you can find *turning points*, which represent relative maximum or relative minimum points.

Example Graph $f(x) = x^3 + 6x^2 - 3$. Estimate the x-coordinates at which the relative maxima and minima occur.

Make a table of values and graph the function.

x	f(x)
-5	22
-4	29
-3	24
-2	13
-1	2
0	-3
1	4
2	29

← indicates a relative maximum

← zero between x = −1, x = 0
← indicates a relative minimum

A relative maximum occurs at x = −4 and a relative minimum occurs at x = 0.

Exercises

Graph each polynomial function. Estimate the x-coordinates at which the relative maxima and relative minima occur.

1. $f(x) = x^3 - 3x^2$

max. at 0, min. at 2

2. $f(x) = 2x^3 + x^2 - 3x$

max. about −1, min. about 0.5

3. $f(x) = 2x^3 - 3x + 2$

max. about −1, min. about 1

4. $f(x) = x^4 - 7x - 3$

min. about 1

5. $f(x) = x^5 - 2x^2 + 2$

max. at 0, min. about 1

6. $f(x) = x^3 + 2x^2 - 3$

max. about −1, min. at 0

Answers (Lesson 6-4)

6-4 Word Problem Practice

Analyzing Graphs of Polynomial Functions

1. LANDSCAPES Jalen uses a fourth-degree polynomial to describe the shape of two hills in the background of a video game that he is helping to write. The graph of the polynomial is shown below.

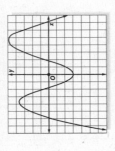

Estimate the x-coordinates at which the relative maxima and relative minima occur.

The relative maxima occur at $x = -3.7$ and $x = 4.5$, and the relative minimum occurs at $x = 0$.

2. NATIONAL PARKS The graph models the cross-section of Mount Rushmore.

Graph Modeling Mount Rushmore

What is the smallest degree possible for the equation that corresponds with this graph?

8

3. VALUE A banker models the expected value of a company in millions of dollars by the formula $n^3 - 3n^2$, where n is the number of years in business. Sketch a graph of $v = n^3 - 3n^2$.

4. CONSECUTIVE NUMBERS Ms. Sanchez asks her students to write expressions to represent five consecutive integers. One solution is $x - 2$, $x - 1$, x, $x + 1$, and $x + 2$. The product of these five consecutive integers is given by the fifth degree polynomial $f(x) = x^5 - 5x^3 + 4x$.

a. For what values of x is $f(x) = 0$?

-2, -1, 0, 1, and 2

b. Sketch the graph of $y = f(x)$.

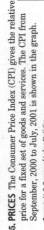

6-4 Practice

Analyzing Graphs of Polynomial Functions

Complete each of the following.
a. Graph each function by making a table of values.
b. Determine the consecutive values of x between which each real zero is located.
c. Estimate the x-coordinates at which the relative maxima and minima occur.

1. $f(x) = -x^3 + 3x^2 - 3$

x	f(x)
-2	-17
-1	1
0	-3
1	-1
2	1
3	-3
4	-19

zeros between −1 and 0, 1 and 2, and 2 and 3; rel. max. at x = 2, rel. min. at x = 0

2. $f(x) = x^3 - 1.5x^2 - 6x + 1$

x	f(x)
-2	-1
-1	4.5
0	1
1	-5.5
2	-9
3	-3.5
4	-17

zeros between −2 and −1, 0 and 1, and 3 and 4; rel. max. at x = −1, rel. min. at x = 2

3. $f(x) = 0.75 x^4 + x^3 - 3x^2 + 4$

x	f(x)
-3	10.75
-2	-4
-1	0.75
0	4
1	2.75
2	12

zeros between −3 and −2, and −2 and −1; rel. max. at x = 0, rel. min. at x = −2 and x = 1

4. $f(x) = x^4 + 4x^3 + 6x^2 + 4x - 3$

x	f(x)
-3	12
-2	-3
-1	-4
0	-3
1	12
2	77

zeros between −3 and −2, and 0 and 1; rel. min. at x = −1

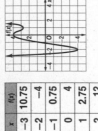

5. PRICES The Consumer Price Index (CPI) gives the relative price for a fixed set of goods and services. The CPI from September, 2000 to July, 2001 is shown in the graph.
Source: U.S. Bureau of Labor Statistics

a. Describe the turning points of the graph. **rel. max. in Nov. and June; rel. min in Dec.**

b. If the graph were modeled by a polynomial equation, what is the least degree the equation could have? **4**

6. LABOR A town's jobless rate can be modeled by (1, 3.3), (2, 4.9), (3, 5.3), (4, 6.4), (5, 4.5), (6, 5.6), (7, 2.5), and (8, 2.7). How many turning points would the graph of a polynomial function through these points have? Describe them.
4: 2 rel. max. and 2 rel. min.

Lesson 6-5 page

6-5 Study Guide and Intervention

Solving Polynomial Equations

Factor Polynomials

Techniques for Factoring Polynomials	
For any number of terms, check for:	greatest common factor
For two terms, check for:	Difference of two squares $a^2 - b^2 = (a + b)(a - b)$ Sum of two cubes $a^3 + b^3 = (a + b)(a^2 - ab + b^2)$ Difference of two cubes $a^3 - b^3 = (a - b)(a^2 + ab + b^2)$
For three terms, check for:	Perfect square trinomials $a^2 + 2ab + b^2 = (a + b)^2$ $a^2 - 2ab + b^2 = (a - b)^2$ General trinomials $acx^2 + (ad + bc)x + bd = (ax + b)(cx + d)$
For four or more terms, check for:	Grouping $ax + bx + ay + by = x(a + b) + y(a + b)$ $= (a + b)(x + y)$

Example   **Factor $24x^2 - 42x - 45$.**

First factor out the GCF to get $24x^2 - 42x - 45 = 3(8x^2 - 14x - 15)$. To find the coefficients of the x terms, you must find two numbers whose product is $8 \cdot (-15) = -120$ and whose sum is -14. The two coefficients must be -20 and 6. Rewrite the expression using $-20x$ and $6x$ and factor by grouping.

$8x^2 - 14x - 15 = 8x^2 - 20x + 6x - 15$ Group to find a GCF.
$= 4x(2x - 5) + 3(2x - 5)$ Factor the GCF of each binomial.
$= (4x + 3)(2x - 5)$ Distributive Property

Thus, $24x^2 - 42x - 45 = 3(4x + 3)(2x - 5)$.

Exercises

Factor completely. If the polynomial is not factorable, write *prime*.

1. $14x^2y^2 + 42xy^3$
$14xy^2(x + 3y)$

2. $6mn + 18m - n - 3$
$(6m - 1)(n + 3)$

3. $2x^2 - 18x + 16$
$2(x + 8)(x + 1)$

4. $x^4 - 1$
$(x^2 + 1)(x + 1)(x - 1)$

5. $35x^3y^4 - 60x^4y$
$5x^3y(7y^3 - 12x)$

6. $2x^3 - 250$
$2(r + 5)(r^2 - 5r + 25)$

7. $100m^8 - 9$
$(10m^4 - 3)(10m^4 + 3)$

8. $x^2 + x + 1$
prime

9. $c^4 + c^3 - c^2 - c$
$c(c + 1)^2(c - 1)$

Lesson 6-4 page

6-4 Enrichment

Golden Rectangles

Use a straightedge, a compass, and the instructions below to construct a golden rectangle.

1. Construct square $ABCD$ with sides of 2 centimeters.

2. Construct the midpoint of $\overline{AB}$. Call the midpoint M.

3. Using M as the center, set your compass opening at MC. Construct an arc with center M that intersects $\overline{AB}$. Call the point of intersection P.

4. Construct a line through P that is perpendicular to $\overline{AB}$.

5. Extend DC so that it intersects the perpendicular. Call the intersection point Q. $APQD$ is a golden rectangle. Check this conclusion by finding the value of $\dfrac{QP}{AP}$.   **0.62**

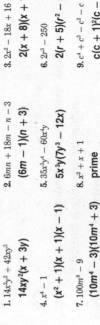

A figure consisting of similar golden rectangles is shown below. Use a compass and the instructions below to draw quarter-circle arcs that form a spiral like that found in the shell of a chambered nautilus.

6. Using A as a center, draw an arc that passes through B and C.

7. Using D as a center, draw an arc that passes through C and E.

8. Using F as a center, draw an arc that passes through E and G.

9. Continue drawing arcs, using $H, K,$ and M as the centers.

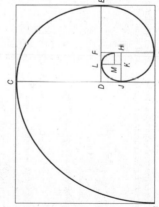

Lesson 6-5 — Skills Practice

6-5 Skills Practice

Solving Polynomial Equations

Factor completely. If the polynomial is not factorable, write *prime*.

1. $7x^2 - 14x$
  $7x(x - 2)$

2. $19x^3 - 38x^2$
  $19x^2(x - 2)$

3. $21x^3 - 18x^2y + 24xy^2$
  $3x(7x^2 - 6xy + 8y^2)$

4. $8j^3k - 4j^4k^3 - 7$
  prime

5. $a^2 + 7a - 18$
  $(a + 9)(a - 2)$

6. $2ak - 6a + k - 3$
  $(2a + 1)(k - 3)$

7. $b^2 + 8b + 7$
  $(b + 7)(b + 1)$

8. $z^2 - 8z - 10$
  prime

9. $4f^2 - 64$
  $4(f + 4)(f - 4)$

10. $d^2 - 12d + 36$
  $(d - 6)^2$

11. $9x^2 + 25$
  prime

12. $y^2 + 18y + 81$
  $(y + 9)^2$

13. $n^3 - 125$
  $(n - 5)(n^2 + 5n + 25)$

14. $m^4 - 1$
  $(m^2 + 1)(m - 1)(m + 1)$

Write each expression in quadratic form, if possible.

15. $5x^4 + 2x^2 - 8$ $5(x^2)^2 + 2(x^2) - 8$

16. $3y^8 - 4y^2 + 3$ **not possible**

17. $100a^6 + a^3$ $100(a^3)^2 + a^3$

18. $x^8 + 4x^4 + 9$ $(x^4)^2 + 4(x^4) + 9$

19. $12x^4 - 7x^2$ $12(x^2)^2 - 7(x^2)$

20. $6b^5 + 3b^3 - 1$ **not possible**

Solve each equation.

21. $a^3 - 9a^2 + 14a = 0$ **0, 7, 2**

22. $x^3 = 3x^2$ **0, 3**

23. $t^4 - 3t^3 - 40t^2 = 0$ **0, -5, 8**

24. $b^3 - 8b^2 + 16b = 0$ **0, 4**

Study Guide and Intervention

6-5 Study Guide and Intervention *(continued)*

Solving Polynomial Equations

Solve Polynomial Equations If a polynomial expression can be written in quadratic form, then you can use what you know about solving quadratic equations to solve the related polynomial equation.

Example 1 Solve $x^4 - 40x^2 + 144 = 0$.

$x^4 - 40x^2 + 144 = 0$ Original equation

$(x^2)^2 - 40(x^2) + 144 = 0$ Write the expression on the left in quadratic form.

$(x^2 - 4)(x^2 - 36) = 0$ Factor.

$x^2 - 4 = 0$ or $x^2 - 36 = 0$ Zero Product Property

$(x - 2)(x + 2) = 0$ or $(x - 6)(x + 6) = 0$ Factor.

$x - 2 = 0$ or $x + 2 = 0$ or $x - 6 = 0$ or $x + 6 = 0$ Zero Product Property

$x = 2$ or $x = -2$ or $x = 6$ or $x = -6$ Simplify.

The solutions are ± 2 and ± 6.

Example 2 Solve $2x + \sqrt{x} - 15 = 0$.

$2x + \sqrt{x} - 15 = 0$ Original equation

$2(\sqrt{x})^2 + \sqrt{x} - 15 = 0$ Write the expression on the left in quadratic form.

$(2\sqrt{x} - 5)(\sqrt{x} + 3) = 0$ Factor.

$2\sqrt{x} - 5 = 0$ or $\sqrt{x} + 3 = 0$ Zero Product Property

$\sqrt{x} = \frac{5}{2}$ or $\sqrt{x} = -3$ Simplify.

Since the principal square root of a number cannot be negative, $\sqrt{x} = -3$ has no solution.
The solution is $\frac{25}{4}$ or $6\frac{1}{4}$.

Exercises

Solve each equation.

1. $x^4 = 49$
  $\pm\sqrt{7}, \pm i\sqrt{7}$

2. $x^4 - 6x^2 = -8$
  $\pm 2, \pm\sqrt{2}$

3. $x^4 - 3x^2 = 54$
  $\pm 3, \pm i\sqrt{6}$

4. $3t^6 - 48t^2 = 0$
  $0, \pm 2, \pm 2i$

5. $m^6 - 16m^3 + 64 = 0$
  $2, -1 \pm i\sqrt{3}$

6. $y^4 - 5y^2 + 4 = 0$
  $\pm 1, \pm 2$

7. $x^4 - 29x^2 + 100 = 0$
  $\pm 5, \pm 2$

8. $4x^4 - 73x^2 + 144 = 0$
  $\pm 4, \pm\frac{3}{2}$

9. $\frac{1}{x^2} - \frac{7}{x} + 12 = 0$
  $\frac{1}{3}, \frac{1}{4}$

10. $x - 5\sqrt{x} + 6 = 0$
  $4, 9$

11. $x - 10\sqrt{x} + 21 = 0$
  $9, 49$

12. $x^{\frac{2}{3}} - 5x^{\frac{1}{3}} + 6 = 0$
  $27, 8$

Answers (Lesson 6-5)

NAME _____ DATE _____ PERIOD _____

6-5 Practice

Solving Polynomial Equations

Factor completely. If the polynomial is not factorable, write prime.

1. $15a^2b - 10ab^2$
   $5ab(3a - 2b)$

2. $3st^2 - 9s^2t + 6s^2t^2$
   $3st(t - 3s^2 + 2st)$

3. $3x^3y^2 - 2x^2y + 5xy$
   $xy(3x^2y - 2x + 5)$

4. $2x^3y - x^2y + 5xy^2 + xy^3$
   $xy(2x^2 - x + 5y + y^2)$

5. $21 - 7t + 3r - rt$
   $(7 + r)(3 - t)$

6. $x^2 - xy + 2x - 2y$
   $(x + 2)(x - y)$

7. $y^3 + 20y + 96$
   $(y + 8)(y + 12)$

8. $4ab + 2a + 6b + 3$
   $(2a + 3)(2b + 1)$

9. $9x^2 - 11n - 2$
   $(6n + 1)(n - 2)$

10. $6x^2 + 7x - 3$
    $(3x - 1)(2x + 3)$

11. $x^2 - 8x - 8$
    prime

12. $6p^2 - 17p - 45$
    $(2p - 9)(3p + 5)$

Write each expression in quadratic form, if possible.

13. $10b^4 + 3b^2 - 11$
    $10(b^2)^2 + 3(b^2) - 11$

14. $-5x^8 + x^2 + 6$
    not possible

15. $28d^6 + 25d^3$
    $28(d^3)^2 + 25(d^3)$

16. $4s^8 + 4s^4 + 7$
    $4(s^4)^2 + 4(s^4) + 7$

17. $500x^4 - x^2$
    $500(x^2)^2 - x^2$

18. $8b^5 - 8b^3 - 1$
    not possible

Solve each equation.

19. $y^4 - 7y^3 - 18y^2 = 0$ **$-2, 0, 9$**

20. $s^5 + 4s^4 - 32s^3 = 0$ **$-8, 0, 4$**

21. $m^4 - 625 = 0$ **$-5, 5, -5i, 5i$**

22. $n^4 - 49n^2 = 0$ **$0, -7, 7$**

23. $x^4 - 50x^2 + 49 = 0$ **$-1, 1, -7, 7$**

24. $t^4 - 21t^2 + 80 = 0$ **$-4, 4, \sqrt{5}, -\sqrt{5}$**

25. **PHYSICS** A proton in a magnetic field follows a path on a coordinate grid modeled by the function $f(x) = x^4 - 2x^2 - 15$. What are the x-coordinates of the points on the grid where the proton crosses the x-axis? **$-\sqrt{5}, \sqrt{5}$**

26. **SURVEYING** Vista county is setting aside a large parcel of land to preserve it as open space. The county has hired Meghan's surveying firm to survey the parcel, which is in the shape of a right triangle. The longer leg of the triangle measures 5 miles less than the square of the shorter leg, and the hypotenuse of the triangle measures 13 miles less than twice the square of the shorter leg. The length of each boundary is a whole number. Find the length of each boundary. **3 mi, 4 mi, 5 mi**

NAME _____ DATE _____ PERIOD _____

6-5 Word Problem Practice

Solving Polynomial Equations

1. **CODES** Marisa has been trying to discover the secret code for a lock. After a long investigation, she discovers that the numbers in the secret code are solutions of the polynomial equation $x^4 - 68x^3 + 1557x^2 - 13770x + 37800 = 0$. After more work, Marisa found that $x^4 - 68x^3 + 1557x^2 - 13770x + 37800 = (x - 5)(x - 12)(x - 21)(x - 30)$. What are the numbers in the secret code?
   5, 12, 21, and 30

2. **OUTPUT** Eduardo is a mechanical engineer. For one of his projects, he had to solve the polynomial equation
   $$m^6 + 5m^3 - 10 = 0.$$
   Write the polynomial $m^6 + 5m^3 - 10$ in quadratic form.
   $(m^3)^2 + 5(m^3) - 10$

3. **VOLUME** A standard shipping box measures x inches high. The width is 3.5 inches more than the height, and the length is 3 inches less than the height. The volume of the box is 561 cubic inches.

   What is x?
   8.5

4. **ROBOTS** A robot explorer's distance from its starting location is given by the polynomial $t^4 - 29t^3 + 100t$, where t is time measured in hours.

   Factor this polynomial.
   $t(t - 2)(t - 5)(t + 2)(t + 5)$

5. **PACKAGING** A small box is placed inside a larger box. The dimensions of the small box are $x + 1$ by $x - 2$ by $x - 1$. The dimensions of the larger box are $2x$ by $x + 4$ by $x + 2$.

   a. Write an expression for the volume of the space inside the larger box but outside the smaller box.
   $x^3 + 10x^2 + 17x + 2$

   b. If the volume of the space inside the larger box but outside the smaller box is equal to $33x + 162$ cubic units, what is x?
   4

   c. What is the volume of the smaller box?
   90 units^3

   d. What is the volume of the larger box?
   384 units^3

Lesson 6-6

NAME _____ DATE _____ PERIOD _____

6-6 Study Guide and Intervention

The Remainder and Factor Theorems

Synthetic Substitution

Remainder Theorem	The remainder, when you divide the polynomial $f(x)$ by $(x - a)$, is the constant $f(a)$. $f(x) = q(x) \cdot (x - a) + f(a)$, where $q(x)$ is a polynomial with degree one less than the degree of $f(x)$.

Example 1 If $f(x) = 3x^4 + 2x^3 - 5x^2 + x - 2$, find $f(-2)$.

Method 1 Synthetic Substitution

By the Remainder Theorem, $f(-2)$ should be the remainder when you divide the polynomial by $x + 2$.

$$
\begin{array}{r|rrrrr}
-2 & 3 & 2 & -5 & 1 & -2 \\
  &   & -6 & 8 & -6 & 10 \\
\hline
  & 3 & -4 & 3 & -5 & 8
\end{array}
$$

The remainder is 8, so $f(-2) = 8$.

Method 2 Direct Substitution

Replace x with -2.

$f(x) = 3x^4 + 2x^3 - 5x^2 + x - 2$
$f(-2) = 3(-2)^4 + 2(-2)^3 - 5(-2)^2 + (-2) - 2$
$= 48 - 16 - 20 - 2 - 2$ or 8

So $f(-2) = 8$.

Example 2 If $f(x) = 5x^3 + 2x - 1$, find $f(3)$.

Again, by the Remainder Theorem, $f(3)$ should be the remainder when you divide the polynomial by $x - 3$.

$$
\begin{array}{r|rrrr}
3 & 5 & 0 & 2 & -1 \\
  &   & 15 & 45 & 141 \\
\hline
  & 5 & 15 & 47 & 140
\end{array}
$$

The remainder is 140, so $f(3) = 140$.

Exercises

Use synthetic substitution to find $f(-5)$ and $f\left(\frac{1}{2}\right)$ for each function.

1. $f(x) = -3x^2 + 5x - 1$ $-101; \dfrac{3}{4}$

2. $f(x) = 4x^2 + 6x - 7$ $63; -3$

3. $f(x) = -x^3 + 3x^2 - 5$ $195; -\dfrac{35}{8}$

4. $f(x) = x^4 + 11x^2 - 1$ $899; \dfrac{29}{16}$

Use synthetic substitution to find $f(4)$ and $f(-3)$ for each function.

5. $f(x) = 2x^2 + x^2 - 5x + 3$ $127; -27$

6. $f(x) = 3x^3 - 4x + 2$ $178; -67$

7. $f(x) = 5x^3 - 4x^2 + 2$ $258; -169$

8. $f(x) = 2x^4 - 4x^3 + 3x^2 + x - 6$ $302; 288$

9. $f(x) = 5x^4 + 3x^3 - 4x^2 - 2x + 4$ $1404; 298$

10. $f(x) = 3x^4 - 2x^3 - x^2 + 2x - 5$ $627; 277$

11. $f(x) = 2x^4 - 4x^3 - x^2 - 6x + 3$ $219; 282$

12. $f(x) = 4x^4 - 4x^3 + 3x^2 - 2x - 3$ $805; 462$

Chapter 6   35   *Glencoe Algebra 2*

NAME _____ DATE _____ PERIOD _____

6-5 Enrichment

History of Quadratic Equations

The ancient Babylonians are believed to be the first to solve quadratic equations, around 400 B.C. Euclid, who devised a geometrical approach in 300 B.C., followed them. Around 598–665 A.D., a Hindu mathematician named Brahmagupta created an almost modern method for solving equations. Finally, around 800 A.D., an Arab mathematician named al-Khwarizmi created a classification of quadratic equations. He classified them into six different categories and devoted a chapter to each type. His equations are made up of three different types of expressions: roots (x), squares of roots (x^2) and numbers.

For example, his first classification was squares equal to roots. A sample of this type of equations is: $x^2 = 2x$.

Now solve this quadratic equation.

$x^2 = 2x$

$x^2 - 2x = 0$ Subtract $2x$ from each side.

$x(x - 2) = 0$ Factor.

$x = 0$ or $x - 2 = 0$ Set both factors equal to 0.

So, $x = 0$ or 2.   Solve.

Write and solve a sample problem for the remaining 5 classifications of quadratic equations, according to al-Khwarizmi.

1. Squares equal to numbers.

   Sample Answer: $x^2 = 25$; $x = -5$ and 5

2. Roots equal to numbers.

   Sample Answer: $2x = 20$; $x = 10$

3. Squares and roots equal to numbers.

   Sample Answer: $x^2 + 10x = 39$; $x = -13$ and $x = 3$

4. Squares and numbers equal to roots.

   Sample Answer: $x^2 + 21 = 10x$; $x = 3$ and $x = 7$

5. Roots and numbers equal to squares.

   Sample Answer: $3x + 4 = x^2$; $x = -1$ and $x = 4$

Chapter 6   34   *Glencoe Algebra 2*

6-6 Skills Practice

The Remainder and Factor Theorems

Use synthetic substitution to find $f(2)$ and $f(-1)$ for each function.

1. $f(x) = x^2 + 6x + 5$ **21, 0**
2. $f(x) = x^2 - x + 1$ **3, 3**
3. $f(x) = x^2 - 2x - 2$ **-2, 1**
4. $f(x) = x^3 + 2x^2 + 5$ **21, 6**
5. $f(x) = x^3 - x^2 - 2x + 3$ **3, 3**
6. $f(x) = x^3 + 6x^2 + x - 4$ **30, 0**
7. $f(x) = x^3 - 3x^2 + x - 2$ **-4, -7**
8. $f(x) = x^3 - 5x^2 - x + 6$ **-8, 1**
9. $f(x) = x^4 + 2x^2 - 9$ **15, -6**
10. $f(x) = x^4 - 3x^3 + 2x^2 - 2x + 6$ **2, 14**
11. $f(x) = x^5 - 7x^3 - 4x + 10$ **-22, 20**
12. $f(x) = x^6 - 2x^5 + x^4 + x^3 - 9x^2 - 20$ **-32, -26**

Given a polynomial and one of its factors, find the remaining factors of the polynomial.

13. $x^3 + 2x^2 - x - 2$; $x + 1$ **x − 1, x + 2**
14. $x^3 + x^2 - 5x + 3$; $x - 1$ **x − 1, x + 3**
15. $x^3 + 3x^2 - 4x - 12$; $x + 3$ **x − 2, x + 2**
16. $x^3 - 6x^2 + 11x - 6$; $x - 3$ **x − 1, x − 2**
17. $x^3 + 2x^2 - 33x - 90$; $x + 5$ **x + 3, x − 6**
18. $x^3 - 6x^2 + 32$; $x - 4$ **x − 4, x + 2**
19. $x^3 - x^2 - 10x - 8$; $x + 2$ **x + 1, x − 4**
20. $x^3 - 19x + 30$; $x - 2$ **x + 5, x − 3**
21. $2x^3 + x^2 - 2x - 1$; $x + 1$ **2x + 1, x − 1**
22. $2x^3 + x^2 - 5x + 2$; $x + 2$ **x − 1, 2x − 1**
23. $3x^3 + 4x^2 - 5x - 2$; $3x + 1$ **x − 1, x + 2**
24. $3x^3 + x^2 + x - 2$; $3x - 2$ **x² + x + 1**

6-6 Study Guide and Intervention (continued)

The Remainder and Factor Theorems

Factors of Polynomials The Factor Theorem can help you find all the factors of a polynomial.

| Factor Theorem | The binomial $x - a$ is a factor of the polynomial $f(x)$ if and only if $f(a) = 0$. |

Example Show that $x + 5$ is a factor of $x^3 + 2x^2 - 13x + 10$. Then find the remaining factors of the polynomial.

By the Factor Theorem, the binomial $x + 5$ is a factor of the polynomial if -5 is a zero of the polynomial function. To check this, use synthetic substitution.

$$
\begin{array}{r|rrrr}
-5 & 1 & 2 & -13 & 10 \\
   &   & -5 & 15 & -10 \\
\hline
   & 1 & -3 & 2 & 0
\end{array}
$$

Since the remainder is 0, $x + 5$ is a factor of the polynomial. The polynomial $x^3 + 2x^2 - 13x + 10$ can be factored as $(x + 5)(x^2 - 3x + 2)$. The depressed polynomial $x^2 - 3x + 2$ can be factored as $(x - 2)(x - 1)$.
So $x^3 + 2x^2 - 13x + 10 = (x + 5)(x - 2)(x - 1)$.

Exercises

Given a polynomial and one of its factors, find the remaining factors of the polynomial.

1. $x^3 + x^2 - 10x + 8$; $x - 2$ **(x + 4)(x − 1)**
2. $x^3 - 4x^2 - 11x + 30$; $x + 3$ **(x − 5)(x − 2)**
3. $x^3 + 15x^2 + 71x + 105$; $x + 7$ **(x + 3)(x + 5)**
4. $x^3 - 7x^2 - 26x + 72$; $x + 4$ **(x − 2)(x − 9)**
5. $2x^3 - x^2 - 7x + 6$; $x - 1$ **(2x − 3)(x + 2)**
6. $3x^3 - x^2 - 62x - 40$; $x + 4$ **(3x + 2)(x − 5)**
7. $12x^3 - 71x^2 + 57x - 10$; $x - 5$ **(4x − 1)(3x − 2)**
8. $14x^3 + x^2 - 24x + 9$; $x - 1$ **(7x − 3)(2x + 3)**
9. $x^3 + x + 10$; $x + 2$ **(x² − 2x + 5)**
10. $2x^3 - 11x^2 + 19x - 28$; $x - 4$ **(2x² − 3x + 7)**
11. $3x^3 - 13x^2 - 34x + 24$; $x - 6$ **(3x² + 5x − 4)**
12. $x^4 + x^3 - 11x^2 - 9x + 18$; $x - 1$ **(x + 2)(x + 3)(x − 3)**

6-6 Word Problem Practice

The Remainder and Factor Theorems

1. HEIGHT A ball tossed into the air follows a parabolic trajectory. Its height after t seconds is given by a polynomial of degree two with leading coefficient -16. Using synthetic substitution, Norman found that the polynomial evaluates to 0 for the values $t = 0$ and $t = 4$. What is the polynomial that describes the ball's height as a function of t?
$-16t^2 + 64t$

2. SYNTHETIC SUBSTITUTION Branford evaluates the polynomial $p(x) = x^3 - 5x^2 + 3x + 5$ for a factor using synthetic substitution. Some of his work is shown below. Unfortunately, the factor and the solution have ink spots over it.

$$\begin{array}{r|rrrr} & 1 & -5 & 3 & 5 \\ & & 11 & 66 & 759 \\ \hline & 1 & 11 & 69 & \blacksquare \end{array}$$

What is the factor he solved for? What is the hidden solution?
11; 764

3. PROFIT The profits of Clyde's Corporation can be modeled by the polynomial $P(y) = y^4 - 4y^3 + 2y^2 + 10y - 200$, where y is the number of years after the business was started. The chief financial officer wants to know the value of $P(10)$. Use synthetic substitution to determine $P(10)$. Show your work.

$$\begin{array}{r|rrrrr} 10| & 1 & -4 & 2 & 10 & -200 \\ & & 10 & 60 & 620 & 6300 \\ \hline & 1 & 6 & 62 & 630 & 6100 \end{array}$$
$P(10) = 6100$

4. EXPONENTIALS The exponential function $t = e^t$ is a special function that you will learn about later. It is not a polynomial function. However, for small values of x, the value of e^x is very closely approximated by the polynomial function
$e(x) = \frac{1}{6}x^3 + \frac{1}{2}x^2 + x + 1$.

Use synthetic substitution to determine $e(0.1)$. Show your work.

$$\begin{array}{r|rrrr} 0.1| & \frac{1}{6} & \frac{1}{2} & 1 & 1 \\ & & \frac{1}{60} & \frac{31}{600} & \frac{631}{6000} \\ \hline & \frac{1}{6} & \frac{31}{60} & \frac{631}{600} & \frac{6631}{6000} \end{array}$$
$1\,\frac{631}{6000}$

5. VOLUME The volume in cubic feet of one popular size of above-ground pool is given by the polynomial
$v(x) = \pi(x^3 - 5x^2 - 80x + 360)$.

a. Use synthetic division to show that $x - 4$ is a factor of $v(x)$. Show your work.
See students' work.

b. Factor $v(x)$ completely.
$\pi(x - 4)(x + 9)(x - 10)$

c. What is the value of $v(10)$?
0

6-6 Practice

The Remainder and Factor Theorems

Use synthetic substitution to find $f(-3)$ and $f(4)$ for each function.

1. $f(x) = x^2 + 2x + 3$ **6, 27**
2. $f(x) = x^2 - 5x + 10$ **34, 6**
3. $f(x) = x^2 - 5x - 4$ **20, −8**
4. $f(x) = x^3 - x^2 - 2x + 3$ **−27, 43**
5. $f(x) = x^3 + 2x^2 + 5$ **−4, 101**
6. $f(x) = x^3 - 6x^2 + 2x$ **−87, −24**
7. $f(x) = x^3 - 2x^2 - 2x + 8$ **−31, 32**
8. $f(x) = x^3 - x^2 + 4x - 4$ **−52, 60**
9. $f(x) = x^3 + 3x^2 + 2x - 50$ **−56, 70**
10. $f(x) = x^4 + x^3 - 3x^2 - x + 12$ **42, 280**
11. $f(x) = x^4 - 2x^2 - x + 7$ **73, 227**
12. $f(x) = 2x^4 - 3x^3 + 4x^2 - 2x + 1$ **286, 377**
13. $f(x) = 2x^4 - x^3 + 2x^2 - 26$ **181, 454**
14. $f(x) = 3x^4 - 4x^3 + 3x^2 - 5x - 3$ **390, 537**
15. $f(x) = x^5 + 7x^3 - 4x - 10$ **−430, 1446**
16. $f(x) = x^6 + 2x^5 - x^4 + x^3 - 9x^2 + 20$ **74, 5828**

Given a polynomial and one of its factors, find the remaining factors of the polynomial.

17. $x^3 + 3x^2 - 6x - 8$; $x - 2$ **x + 1, x + 4**
18. $x^3 + 7x^2 + 7x - 15$; $x - 1$ **x + 3, x + 5**
19. $x^3 - 9x^2 + 27x - 27$; $x - 3$ **x − 3, x − 3**
20. $x^3 - x^2 - 8x + 12$; $x + 3$ **x − 2, x − 2**
21. $x^3 + 5x^2 - 2x - 24$; $x - 2$ **x + 3, x + 4**
22. $x^3 - x^2 - 14x + 24$; $x + 4$ **x − 3, x − 2**
23. $3x^3 - 4x^2 - 17x + 6$; $x + 2$ **x − 3, 3x − 1**
24. $4x^3 - 12x^2 - x + 3$; $x - 3$ **2x − 1, 2x + 1**
25. $18x^3 + 9x^2 - 2x - 1$; $2x + 1$ **3x + 1, 3x − 1**
26. $6x^3 + 5x^2 - 3x - 2$; $3x - 2$ **2x + 1, x + 1**
27. $x^5 + x^4 - 5x^3 - 5x^2 + 4x + 4$; $x + 1$ **x − 1, x + 1, x − 2, x + 2**
28. $x^5 - 2x^4 + 4x^3 - 8x^2 - 5x + 10$; $x - 2$ **x − 1, x + 1, x² + 5**

29. **POPULATION** The projected population in thousands for a city over the next several years can be estimated by the function $P(x) = x^3 + 2x^2 - 8x + 520$, where x is the number of years since 2005. Use synthetic substitution to estimate the population for 2010. **655,000**

30. **VOLUME** The volume of water in a rectangular swimming pool can be modeled by the polynomial $2x^3 - 9x^2 + 7x + 6$. If the depth of the pool is given by the polynomial $2x + 1$, what polynomials express the length and width of the pool? **x − 3 and x − 2**

NAME _____ DATE _____ PERIOD _____

6-7 Study Guide and Intervention

Roots and Zeros

Synthetic Types of Roots The following statements are equivalent for any polynomial function $f(x)$.

- c is a zero of the polynomial function $f(x)$.
- c is a root or solution of the polynomial equation $f(x) = 0$.
- $(x - c)$ is a factor of the polynomial $f(x)$.
- If c is real, then $(c, 0)$ is an intercept of the graph of $f(x)$.

Fundamental Theorem of Algebra	Every polynomial equation with degree greater than zero has at least one root in the set of complex numbers.
Corollary to the Fundamental Theorem of Algebras	A polynomial equation of the form $P(x) = 0$ of degree n with complex coefficients has exactly n roots in the set of complex numbers, including repeated roots.
Descartes' Rule of Signs	If $P(x)$ is a polynomial with real coefficients whose terms are arranged in descending powers of the variable, • the number of positive real zeros of $y = P(x)$ is the same as the number of changes in sign of the coefficients of the terms, or is less than this by an even number, and • the number of negative real zeros of $y = P(x)$ is the same as the number of changes in sign of the coefficients of the terms of $P(-x)$, or is less than this number by an even number.

Example 1 Solve the equation $6x^3 + 3x = 0$. State the number and type of roots.

$6x^3 + 3x = 0$

$3x(2x^2 + 1) = 0$

Use the Zero Product Property.

$3x = 0$ or $2x^2 + 1 = 0$

$x = 0$ or $2x^2 = -1$

$x = \pm \dfrac{i\sqrt{2}}{2}$

The equation has one real root, 0, and two imaginary roots, $\pm \dfrac{i\sqrt{2}}{2}$.

Example 2 State the number of positive real zeros, negative real zeros, and imaginary zeros for $p(x) = 4x^4 - 3x^3 - x^2 + 2x - 5$.

Since $p(x)$ has degree 4, it has 4 zeros.

Since there are three sign changes, there are 3 or 1 positive real zeros.

Find $p(-x)$ and count the number of changes in sign for its coefficients.

$p(-x) = 4(-x)^4 - 3(-x)^3 + (-x)^2 + 2(-x) - 5$

$= 4x^4 + 3x^3 + x^2 - 2x - 5$

Since there is one sign change, there is exactly 1 negative real zero.

Thus, there are 3 positive and 1 negative real zero or 1 positive and 1 negative real zeros and 2 imaginary zeros.

Exercises

Solve each equation. State the number and type of roots.

1. $x^2 + 4x - 21 = 0$ 2. $2x^3 - 50x = 0$ 3. $12x^3 + 100x = 0$

   3, −7; 2 real   0, ±5; 3 real $0, \pm \dfrac{5i\sqrt{3}}{3}$, 1 real, 2 imaginary

State the possible number of positive real zeros, negative real zeros, and imaginary zeros for each function.

4. $f(x) = 3x^3 + x^2 - 8x - 12$ 5. $f(x) = 3x^5 - x^4 - x^3 + 6x^2 - 5$

   1; 2 or 0; 0 or 2   3 or 1; 2 or 0; 0, 2, or 4

NAME _____ DATE _____ PERIOD _____

6-6 Enrichment

Radical Notation

In 1494, the first Edition of *Summa de arithmetica geometrica proprtioni et proportionalita*, now known as the *Suma*, was printed in Italy. The author, Luca Pacioli, wrote the book as a summary of the mathematical knowledge at the time. However, the notation used in the book is quite similar to the notation used today. For example, to represent radicals, the following was used:

6 . p . R . 10

In our notation, the p represents "plus" and the R represents "radical." So, 6 . p . R . 10 means $6 + \sqrt{10}$.

1. What letter would you expect to represent subtraction?

   m

2. Translate the following notations into modern notation.

a. 18 . m . R . 90

   $18 - \sqrt{90}$

b. 108 . m . R . 3240 . p . R . 3240 . m . R . 900

   $108 - \sqrt{3240} + \sqrt{3240} - \sqrt{900}$

c. 10 . R . 5 . p . 2 . R . 3

   $10\sqrt{5} + 2\sqrt{3}$

3. Translate the following into notations from 1494.

a. $32\sqrt{10}$

   32 . R . 10

b. $21\sqrt{6} + 3\sqrt{3}$

   21 . R . 6 . p . 3 . R . 3

c. $5\sqrt{2} - 2 + 7\sqrt{11}$

   5 . R . 2 . m . 2 . p . 7 . R . 11

Lesson 6-7

6-7 Skills Practice

Roots and Zeros

Solve each equation. State the number and type of roots.

1. $5x + 12 = 0$

$-\dfrac{12}{5}$; 1 real

2. $x^2 - 4x + 40 = 0$

$2 \pm 6i$; 2 imaginary

3. $x^5 + 4x^3 = 0$

0, 0, 0, $2i$, $-2i$; 3 real, 2 imaginary

4. $x^4 - 625 = 0$

5, $5i$, $-5i$, -5; 2 real, 2 imaginary

5. $4x^2 - 4x - 1 = 0$

$\dfrac{1 \pm \sqrt{2}}{2}$; 2 real

6. $x^5 - 81x = 0$

0, -3, 3, $-3i$, $3i$; 3 real, 2 imaginary

State the possible number of positive real zeros, negative real zeros, and imaginary zeros of each function.

7. $g(x) = 3x^3 - 4x^2 - 17x + 6$

2 or 0; 1; 2 or 0

8. $h(x) = 4x^3 - 12x^2 - x + 3$

2 or 0; 1; 2 or 0

9. $f(x) = x^3 - 8x^2 + 2x - 4$

3 or 1; 0; 2 or 0

10. $p(x) = x^3 - x^2 + 4x - 6$

3 or 1; 0; 2 or 0

11. $q(x) = x^4 + 7x^2 + 3x - 9$

1; 1; 2

12. $f(x) = x^4 - x^3 - 5x^2 + 6x + 1$

2 or 0; 2 or 0; 4 or 2 or 0

Find all the zeros of each function.

13. $h(x) = x^3 - 5x^2 + 5x + 3$

$3, 1 + \sqrt{2}, 1 - \sqrt{2}$

14. $g(x) = x^3 - 6x^2 + 13x - 10$

$2, 2 + i, 2 - i$

15. $h(x) = x^3 + 4x^2 + x - 6$

$1, -2, -3$

16. $q(x) = x^3 + 3x^2 - 6x - 8$

$2, -1, -4$

17. $g(x) = x^4 - 3x^3 - 5x^2 + 3x + 4$

$-1, -1, 1, 4$

18. $f(x) = x^4 - 21x^2 + 80$

$-4, 4, -\sqrt{5}, \sqrt{5}$

Write a polynomial function of least degree with integral coefficients that have the given zeros.

19. $-3, -5, 1$

$f(x) = x^3 + 7x^2 + 7x - 15$

20. $3i$

$f(x) = x^2 + 9$

21. $-5 + i$

$f(x) = x^2 + 10x + 26$

22. $-1, \sqrt{3}, -\sqrt{3}$

$f(x) = x^3 + x^2 - 3x - 3$

23. $i, 5i$

$f(x) = x^4 + 26x^2 + 25$

24. $-1, i\sqrt{6}$

$f(x) = x^4 + 5x^2 - 6$

6-7 Study Guide and Intervention (continued)

Roots and Zeros

Find Zeros

Complex Conjugate Theorem	Suppose a and b are real numbers with $b \neq 0$. If $a + bi$ is a zero of a polynomial function with real coefficients, then $a - bi$ is also a zero of the function.

Example Find all of the zeros of $f(x) = x^4 - 15x^2 + 38x - 60$.

Since $f(x)$ has degree 4, the function has 4 zeros.

$f(x) = x^4 - 15x^2 + 38x - 60$ $f(-x) = x^4 - 15x^2 - 38x - 60$

Since there are 3 sign changes for the coefficients of $f(x)$, the function has 3 or 1 positive real zeros. Since there is + sign change for the coefficients of $f(-x)$, the function has 1 negative real zero. Use synthetic substitution to test some possible zeros.

2]	1	0	-15	38	-60
		2	4	-22	32
	1	2	-11	16	-28

3]	1	0	-15	38	-60
		3	9	-18	60
	1	3	-6	20	0

So 3 is a zero of the polynomial function. Now try synthetic substitution again to find a zero of the depressed polynomial.

-2]	1	3	-6	20
		-2	-2	16
	1	1	-8	36

-4]	1	3	-6	20
		-4	4	8
	1	-1	-2	28

-5]	1	3	-6	20
		-5	10	-20
	1	-2	4	0

So -5 is another zero. Use the Quadratic Formula on the depressed polynomial $x^2 - 2x + 4$ to find the other 1 zeros, $1 \pm i\sqrt{3}$.

The function has two real zeros at 3 and -5 and two imaginary zeros at $1 \pm i\sqrt{3}$.

Exercises

Find all zeros of each function.

1. $f(x) = x^3 + x^2 + 9x + 9$ $-1, \pm 3i$

2. $f(x) = x^3 - 3x^2 + 4x - 12$ $3, \pm 2i$

3. $p(a) = a^3 - 10a^2 + 34a - 40$ $4, 3 \pm i$

4. $p(x) = x^3 - 5x^2 + 11x - 15$ $3, 1 \pm 2i$

5. $f(x) = x^3 + 6x + 20$

$-2, 1 \pm 3i$

6. $f(x) = x^4 - 3x^3 + 21x^2 - 75x - 100$

$-1, 4 \pm 5i$

Answers (Lesson 6-7)

6-7 Word Problem Practice

Roots and Zeros

1. TABLES Li Pang made a table of values for the polynomial $p(x)$. Her table is shown below.

x	p(x)
-4	-3
-3	-1
-2	0
-1	2
0	0
1	4
2	0
3	2
4	5

Name three roots of $p(x)$.

-2, 0, and 2

2. ROOTS Ryan is an electrical engineer. He often solves polynomial equations to work out various properties of the circuits he builds. For one circuit, he must find the roots of a polynomial $p(x)$. He finds that $p(2 - 3i) = 0$. Give two different roots of $p(x)$.

2 - 3i and 2 + 3i

3. REAL ROOTS There are more than a thousand roller coasters around the world. Roller coaster designers can use polynomial functions to model the shapes of possible roller coasters. Madison is studying a roller coaster modeled by the polynomial $f(x) = x^6 - 14x^4 + 49x^2 - 36$. She knows that all of the roots of $f(x)$ are real. How many positive and how many negative roots are there? How are the set of positive roots and negative roots related to each other? Explain.

There are 3 positive and 3 negative roots. The set of positive roots is the mirror image of the set of negative roots because the polynomial is even.

4. COMPLEX ROOTS Eric is a statistician. During the course of his work, he had to find something called the "eigenvalues of a matrix," which was basically the same as finding the roots of a polynomial. The polynomial was $x^4 + 6x^2 + 25$. One of the roots of this polynomial is $1 + 2i$. What are the other 3 roots? Explain.

The other 3 roots are $-1 - 2i$, $1 - 2i$, and $-1 + 2i$.
Sample answer: Since $f(x) = f(-x)$, if r is a root, so is $-r$; hence $-1 - 2i$ is a root. Because the coefficients are real, if r is a root, its complex conjugate must also be a root; therefore, $1 - 2i$ and $-1 + 2i$ are also roots.

5. QUADRILATERALS Shayna plotted the four vertices of a quadrilateral in the complex plane and then encoded the points in a polynomial $p(x)$ by making them the roots of $p(x)$. The polynomial $p(x)$ is $x^4 - 9x^3 + 27x^2 + 23x - 150$.

a. The polynomial $p(x)$ has one positive real root, and it is an integer. Find the integer.

3

b. Find the negative real root(s) of $p(x)$.

-2

c. Find the complex roots of $p(x)$.

4 + 3i and 4 - 3i

6-7 Practice

Roots and Zeros

Solve each equation. State the number and type of roots.

1. $-9x - 15 = 0$

$-\dfrac{5}{3}$, **1 real**

2. $x^4 - 5x^2 + 4 = 0$

-1, 1, -2, 2; 4 real

3. $x^5 - 81x = 0$

0, -3, 3, -3i, 3i; 3 real, 2 imaginary

4. $x^3 + x^2 - 3x - 3 = 0$

-1, $-\sqrt{3}$, $\sqrt{3}$; 3 real

5. $x^3 + 6x + 20 = 0$

-2, $1 \pm 3i$; 1 real, 2 imaginary

6. $x^4 - x^3 - x^2 - x - 2 = 0$

2, -1, -i, i; 2 real, 2 imaginary

State the possible number of positive real zeros, negative real zeros, and imaginary zeros of each function.

7. $f(x) = 4x^3 - 2x^2 + x + 3$

2 or 0; 1; 2 or 0

8. $p(x) = 2x^4 - 2x^3 + 2x^2 - x - 1$

3 or 1; 1; 2 or 0

9. $q(x) = 3x^4 + x^3 - 3x^2 + 7x + 5$

2 or 0; 2 or 0; 4, 2, or 0

10. $h(x) = 7x^4 + 3x^3 - 2x^2 - x + 1$

2 or 0; 2 or 0; 4, 2, or 0

Find all zeros of each function.

11. $h(x) = 2x^3 + 3x^2 - 65x + 84$

$-7, \dfrac{3}{2}, 4$

12. $p(x) = x^3 - 3x^2 + 9x - 7$

1, $1 + i\sqrt{6}$, $1 - i\sqrt{6}$

13. $h(x) = x^3 - 7x^2 + 17x - 5$

3, 2 + i, 2 - i

14. $g(x) = x^4 + 50x^2 + 49$

-i, i, -7i, 7i

15. $g(x) = x^4 + 4x^3 - 3x^2 - 14x - 8$

-1, -1, -2, -4

16. $f(x) = x^4 - 6x^3 + 6x^2 + 24x - 40$

-2, 2, 3 - i, 3 + i

Write a polynomial function of least degree with integral coefficients that has the given zeros.

17. $-5, 3i$

$f(x) = x^3 + 5x^2 + 9x + 45$

18. $-2, 3 + i$

$f(x) = x^3 - 4x^2 - 2x + 20$

19. $-1, 4, 3i$

$f(x) = x^4 - 3x^3 + 5x^2 - 27x - 36$

20. $2, 5, 1 + i$

$f(x) = x^4 - 9x^3 + 25x^2 - 34x + 20$

21. CRAFTS Stephan has a set of plans to build a wooden box. He wants to reduce the volume of the box to 105 cubic inches. He would like to reduce the length of each dimension in the plan by the same amount. The plans call for the box to be 10 inches by 8 inches by 6 inches. Write and solve a polynomial equation to find out how much Stephan should take from each dimension. $(10 - x)(8 - x)(6 - x) = 105$; **3 in.**

Lesson 6-8

6-8 Study Guide and Intervention

Rational Zero Theorem

Identify Rational Zeros

Rational Zero Theorem	Let $f(x) = a_n x^n + a_{n-1} x^{n-1} + \ldots + a_1 x + a_0$, represent a polynomial function with integral coefficients. If $\frac{p}{q}$ is a rational number in simplest form and is a zero of $y = f(x)$, then p is a factor of a_0 and q is a factor of a_n.
Corollary (Integral Zero Theorem)	If the coefficients of a polynomial are integers such that $a_n = 1$ and $a_0 \neq 0$, any rational zeros of the function must be factors of a_0.

Example List all of the possible rational zeros of each function.

a. $f(x) = 3x^4 - 2x^2 + 6x - 10$

If $\frac{p}{q}$ is a rational root, then p is a factor of -10 and q is a factor of 3. The possible values for p are $\pm 1, \pm 2, \pm 5,$ and ± 10. The possible values for q are ± 1 and ± 3. So all of the possible rational zeros are $\frac{p}{q} = \pm 1, \pm 2, \pm 5, \pm 10, \pm \frac{1}{3}, \pm \frac{2}{3}, \pm \frac{5}{3},$ and $\pm \frac{10}{3}$.

b. $q(x) = x^3 - 10x^2 + 14x - 36$

Since the coefficient of x^3 is 1, the possible rational zeros must be the factors of the constant term -36. So the possible rational zeros are $\pm 1, \pm 2, \pm 3, \pm 4, \pm 6, \pm 9, \pm 12, \pm 18,$ and ± 36.

Exercises

List all of the possible rational zeros of each function.

1. $f(x) = x^3 + 3x^2 - x + 8$
$\pm 1, \pm 2, \pm 4, \pm 8$

2. $g(x) = x^5 - 7x^4 + 3x^2 + x - 20$
$\pm 1, \pm 2, \pm 4, \pm 5, \pm 10, \pm 20$

3. $h(x) = x^4 - 7x^3 - 4x^2 + x - 49$
$\pm 1, \pm 7, \pm 49$

4. $p(x) = 2x^4 - 5x^3 + 8x^2 + 3x - 5$
$\pm 1, \pm 5, \pm \frac{1}{2}, \pm \frac{5}{2}$

5. $g(x) = 3x^4 - 5x^3 + 10x + 12$
$\pm 1, \pm 2, \pm 3, \pm 4, \pm 6, \pm 12,$
$\pm \frac{1}{3}, \pm \frac{2}{3}, \pm \frac{4}{3}$

6. $r(x) = 4x^5 - 2x + 18$
$\pm 1, \pm 2, \pm 3, \pm 6, \pm 9, \pm 18,$
$\pm \frac{1}{2}, \pm \frac{3}{2}, \pm \frac{9}{2}, \pm \frac{1}{4}, \pm \frac{3}{4}, \pm \frac{9}{4}$

7. $f(x) = x^7 - 6x^5 - 3x^4 + x^3 + 4x^2 - 120$
$\pm 1, \pm 2, \pm 3, \pm 4, \pm 5, \pm 6, \pm 8, \pm 10, \pm 12,$
$\pm 15, \pm 20, \pm 24, \pm 30, \pm 40, \pm 60, \pm 120$

8. $g(x) = 5x^6 - 3x^4 + 5x^3 + 2x^2 - 15$
$\pm 1, \pm 3, \pm 5, \pm 15, \pm \frac{1}{5}, \pm \frac{3}{5}$

9. $h(x) = 6x^5 - 3x^4 + 12x^3 + 18x^2 - 9x + 21$
$\pm 1, \pm 3, \pm 7, \pm 21, \pm \frac{1}{2}, \pm \frac{3}{2}, \pm \frac{7}{2}, \pm \frac{21}{2},$
$\pm \frac{1}{3}, \pm \frac{7}{3}, \pm \frac{1}{6}, \pm \frac{7}{6}$

10. $p(x) = 2x^7 - 3x^6 + 11x^5 - 20x^2 + 11$
$\pm 1, \pm 11, \pm \frac{1}{2}, \pm \frac{11}{2}$

6-7 Enrichment

The Bisection Method for Approximating Real Zeros

The **bisection method** can be used to approximate zeros of polynomial functions like $f(x) = x^3 + x^2 - 3x - 3$.

Since $f(1) = -4$ and $f(2) = 3$, there is at least one real zero between 1 and 2. The midpoint of this interval is $\frac{1+2}{2} = 1.5$. Since $f(1.5) = -1.875$, the zero is between 1.5 and 2. The midpoint of this interval is $\frac{1.5+2}{2} = 1.75$. Since $f(1.75)$ is about 0.172, the zero is between 1.5 and 1.75. The midpoint of this interval is $\frac{1.5+1.75}{2} = 1.625$. The midpoint of this interval is $\frac{1.625 + 1.75}{2} = 1.6875$. Since $f(1.625)$ is about -0.94. The zero is between 1.625 and 1.75. The midpoint of this interval is $\frac{1.625+1.75}{2} = 1.6875$. Since $f(1.6875)$ is about -0.41, the zero is between 1.6875 and 1.75. Therefore, the zero is 1.7 to the nearest tenth.

The diagram below summarizes the results obtained by the bisection method.

Using the bisection method, approximate to the nearest tenth the zero between the two integral values of x for each function.

1. $f(x) = x^3 - 4x^2 - 11x + 2, f(0) = 2, f(1) = -12$ **0.2**

2. $f(x) = 2x^4 + x^2 - 15, f(1) = -12, f(2) = 21$ **1.6**

3. $f(x) = x^5 - 2x^2 - 12, f(1) = -13, f(2) = 4$ **1.9**

4. $f(x) = 4x^3 - 2x + 7, f(-2) = -21, f(-1) = 5$ **-1.3**

5. $f(x) = 3x^3 - 14x^2 - 27x + 126, f(4) = -14, f(5) = 16$ **4.7**

6-8 Study Guide and Intervention (continued)

Rational Zero Theorem

Find Rational Zeros

Example 1 Find all of the rational zeros of $f(x) = 5x^3 + 12x^2 - 29x + 12$.

From the corollary to the Fundamental Theorem of Algebra, we know that there are exactly 3 complex roots. According to Descartes' Rule of Signs there are 2 or 0 positive real roots and 1 negative real root. The possible rational zeros are $\pm 1, \pm 2, \pm 3, \pm 4, \pm 6, \pm 12,$ $\pm\frac{1}{5}, \pm\frac{2}{5}, \pm\frac{3}{5}, \pm\frac{4}{5}, \pm\frac{6}{5}, \pm\frac{12}{5}$. Make a table and test some possible rational zeros.

p/q	5	12	-29	12
1	5	17	-12	0

Since $f(1) = 0$, you know that $x = 1$ is a zero.
The depressed polynomial is $5x^2 + 17x - 12$, which can be factored as $(5x - 3)(x + 4)$.
By the Zero Product Property, this expression equals 0 when $x = \frac{3}{5}$ or $x = -4$.
The rational zeros of this function are $1, \frac{3}{5}$, and -4.

Example 2 Find all of the zeros of $f(x) = 8x^4 + 2x^3 + 5x^2 + 2x - 3$.

There are 4 complex roots, with 1 positive real root and 3 or 1 negative real roots. The possible rational zeros are $\pm 1, \pm 3, \pm\frac{1}{2}, \pm\frac{1}{4}, \pm\frac{1}{8}, \pm\frac{3}{2}, \pm\frac{3}{4}$, and $\pm\frac{3}{8}$.

Make a table and test some possible values.

p/q	8	2	5	2	-3
1	8	10	15	17	14
2	8	18	41	84	165
$\frac{1}{2}$	8	6	8	6	0

Since $f\left(\frac{1}{2}\right) = 0$, we know that $x = \frac{1}{2}$ is a root.

The depressed polynomial is $8x^3 + 6x^2 + 8x + 6$.
Try synthetic substitution again. Any remaining rational roots must be negative.

p/q	8	6	8	6
$-\frac{1}{4}$	8	4	7	$4\frac{1}{4}$
$-\frac{3}{4}$	8	0	8	0

$x = -\frac{3}{4}$ is another rational root.
The depressed polynomial is $8x^2 + 8 = 0$,
which has roots $\pm i$.

The zeros of this function are $\frac{1}{2}, -\frac{3}{4}$ and $\pm i$.

Exercises

Find all of the rational zeros of each function.

1. $f(x) = x^3 + 4x^2 - 25x - 28$ **-1, 4, -7**
2. $f(x) = x^3 + 6x^2 + 4x + 24$ **-6**

Find all of the zeros of each function.

3. $f(x) = x^4 + 2x^3 - 11x^2 + 8x - 60$ **3, -5, ±2i**
4. $f(x) = 4x^4 + 5x^3 + 30x^2 + 45x - 54$ **$\frac{3}{4}$, -2, ±3i**

6-8 Skills Practice

Rational Zero Theorem

List all of the possible rational zeros of each function.

1. $n(x) = x^2 + 5x + 3$
$\pm 1, \pm 3$

2. $h(x) = x^2 - 2x - 5$
$\pm 1, \pm 5$

3. $w(x) = x^2 - 5x + 12$
$\pm 1, \pm 2, \pm 3, \pm 4, \pm 6, \pm 12$

4. $f(x) = 2x^2 + 5x + 3$
$\pm\frac{1}{2}, -\frac{3}{2} \pm 1, \pm 3$

5. $q(x) = 6x^3 + x^2 - x + 2$
$\pm\frac{1}{6}, \pm\frac{1}{3}, \pm\frac{1}{2}, \pm\frac{2}{3}, \pm 1, \pm 2$

6. $g(x) = 9x^4 + 3x^3 + 3x^2 - x + 27$
$\pm\frac{1}{9}, \pm\frac{1}{3}, \pm 1, \pm 3, \pm 9, \pm 27$

Find all of the rational zeros of each function.

7. $f(x) = x^3 - 2x^2 + 5x - 4$
1

8. $g(x) = x^3 - 3x^2 - 4x - 2$
-2, 2, 3

9. $p(x) = x^3 - x^2 + x - 1$
1

10. $z(x) = x^3 - 4x^2 + 6x - 4$
2

11. $h(x) = x^3 - x^2 + 4x - 4$
1

12. $g(x) = 3x^3 - 9x^2 - 10x - 8$
4

13. $g(x) = 2x^3 + 7x^2 - 7x - 12$
-4, -1, $\frac{3}{2}$

14. $h(x) = 2x^3 - 5x^2 - 4x + 3$
-1, $\frac{1}{2}$, 3

15. $p(x) = 3x^3 - 5x^2 - 14x - 4$
$-\frac{1}{3}$

16. $q(x) = 3x^3 + 2x^2 + 27x + 18$
$-\frac{2}{3}$

17. $q(x) = 3x^3 - 7x^2 + 4$
$-\frac{2}{3}$, 1, 2

18. $f(x) = x^4 - 2x^3 - 13x^2 + 14x + 24$
-3, -1, 2, 4

19. $p(x) = x^4 - 5x^3 - 9x^2 - 25x - 70$
-2, 7

20. $n(x) = 16x^4 - 32x^3 - 13x^2 + 29x - 6$
-1, $\frac{1}{4}$, $\frac{3}{4}$, 2

Find all of the zeros of each function.

21. $f(x) = x^3 + 5x^2 + 11x + 15$
-3, -1 + 2i, -1 - 2i

22. $q(x) = x^3 - 10x^2 + 18x - 4$
2, 4 +, $\sqrt{14}$, 4 - $\sqrt{14}$

23. $m(x) = 6x^4 - 17x^3 + 8x^2 + 8x - 3$
$\frac{1}{3}, \frac{3}{2}, \frac{1+\sqrt{5}}{2}, \frac{1-\sqrt{5}}{2}$

24. $g(x) = x^4 + 4x^3 + 5x^2 - 4x + 4$
-2, -2, -i, i

Answers (Lesson 6-8)

Practice page

6-8 Practice
Rational Zero Theorem

List all of the possible rational zeros of each function.

1. $h(x) = x^3 - 5x^2 + 2x + 12$ $\pm1, \pm2, \pm3, \pm4, \pm6, \pm12$

2. $s(x) = x^4 - 8x^3 + 7x - 14$ $\pm1, \pm2, \pm7, \pm14$

3. $f(x) = 3x^5 - 5x^2 + x + 6$ $\pm\frac{1}{3}, \pm\frac{2}{3}, \pm1, \pm2, \pm3, \pm6$

4. $p(x) = 3x^2 + x + 7$ $\pm\frac{1}{3}, \pm\frac{7}{3}, \pm1, \pm7$

5. $g(x) = 5x^3 + x^2 - x + 8$ $\pm\frac{1}{5}, \pm\frac{2}{5}, \pm\frac{4}{5}, \pm\frac{8}{5}, \pm1, \pm2, \pm4, \pm8$

6. $q(x) = 6x^5 + x^3 - 3$ $\pm\frac{1}{6}, \pm\frac{1}{3}, \pm\frac{1}{2}, \pm\frac{2}{3}, \pm\frac{3}{2}, \pm1, \pm3$

Find all of the rational zeros of each function.

7. $q(x) = x^3 + 3x^2 - 6x - 8$ $-4, -1, 2$

8. $v(x) = x^3 - 9x^2 + 27x - 27$ 3

9. $c(x) = x^3 - x^2 - 8x + 12$ $-3, 2$

10. $f(x) = x^4 - 49x^2$ $0, -7, 7$

11. $h(x) = x^3 - 7x^2 + 17x - 15$ 3

12. $b(x) = x^3 + 6x + 20$ -2

13. $f(x) = x^3 - 6x^2 + 4x - 24$ 6

14. $g(x) = 2x^3 + 3x^2 - 4x - 4$ -2

15. $h(x) = 2x^3 - 7x^2 - 21x + 54$ $-3, 2, \frac{9}{2}$

16. $z(x) = x^4 - 3x^3 + 5x^2 - 27x - 36$ $-1, 4$

17. $d(x) = x^4 + x^3 + 16$ **no rational zeros**

18. $n(x) = x^4 - 2x^3 - 3$ -1

19. $p(x) = 2x^4 - 7x^3 + 4x^2 + 7x - 6$ $-1, 1, \frac{3}{2}, 2$

20. $q(x) = 6x^4 - 9x^3 + 40x^2 + 7x - 12$ $-\frac{3}{2}, -\frac{4}{3}$

Find all of the zeros of each function.

21. $f(x) = 2x^4 + 7x^3 - 2x^2 - 19x - 12$ $-1, -3, \frac{1+\sqrt{33}}{4}, \frac{1-\sqrt{33}}{4}$

22. $q(x) = x^4 - 4x^3 + x^2 + 16x - 20$ $-2, 2, 2+i, 2-i$

23. $h(x) = x^6 - 8x^3$ $0, 2, -1+i\sqrt{3}, -1-i\sqrt{3}$

24. $g(x) = x^6 - 1$ $-1, 1, \frac{-1+i\sqrt{3}}{2}, \frac{1+i\sqrt{3}}{2}, \frac{1-i\sqrt{3}}{2}, \frac{-1-i\sqrt{3}}{2}$

25. **TRAVEL** The height of a box that Joan is shipping is 3 inches less than the width of the box. The length is 2 inches more than twice the width. The volume of the box is 1540 in³. What are the dimensions of the box? **22 in. by 10 in. by 7 in.**

26. **GEOMETRY** The height of a square pyramid is 3 meters shorter than the side of its base. If the volume of the pyramid is 432 m³, how tall is it? Use the formula $V = \frac{1}{3}Bh$. **9 m**

Word Problem Practice page

6-8 Word Problem Practice
Rational Zero Theorem

1. **ROOTS** Paul was examining an old algebra book. He came upon a page about polynomial equations and saw the polynomial below.

$x^9 \quad +8$

As you can see, all the middle terms were blotted out by an ink spill. What are all the possible rational roots of this polynomial?
-8, -4, -2, -1, 1, 2, 4, 8

2. **IRRATIONAL CONSTANTS** Cherie was given a polynomial whose constant term was $\sqrt{2}$. Is it possible for this polynomial to have a rational root? If it is not, explain why not. If it is possible, give an example of such a polynomial with a rational root.
Yes, it is possible. For example, the polynomial $x^2 - (1 + \sqrt{2})x + \sqrt{2}$ has 1 as a root.

3. **MARKOV CHAINS** Tara is a mathematician who specializes in probability. In the course of her work, she needed to find the roots of the polynomial
$p(x) = 288x^4 - 288x^3 + 106x^2 - 17x + 1$.
What are the roots of $p(x)$?
$\frac{1}{3}, \frac{1}{4}$ **and** $\frac{1}{6}$

4. **PYRAMIDS** The Great Pyramid in Giza, Egypt has a square base with side lengths of 5x yards and a height of $4x - 50$ yards. The volume of the Great Pyramid is 3,125,000 cubic yards. Use a calculator to find the value of x and the dimensions of the pyramid.
x = 50; length= 250 yards; height= 150 yards

5. **BOXES** Devon made a box with length $x + 1$, width $x + 3$, and height $x - 3$.

a. What is the volume of Devon's box as a function of x?
$V(x) = x^3 + x^2 - 9x - 9$

b. What is x if the volume of the box is equal to 1001 cubic inches?
10

c. What is x if the volume of the box is equal to $14\frac{5}{8}$ cubic inches?
3.5

6-8 Enrichment

Irrational Numbers

Philosopher Hippasus of Metapontum was believed to have discovered that $\sqrt{2}$ was irrational. Mathematicians of the time denied the existence of irrational numbers and killed Hippasus, not wishing to believe this fundamental number could fail to be a ratio of integers.

The typical way to prove that $\sqrt{2}$ is irrational is by contradiction and relies on a few other common facts that are easily proven. That is, the proof assumes that it is rational and deduces a contradiction.

Theorem: $\sqrt{2}$ is irrational

Proof: Suppose $\sqrt{2}$ is a rational number. Then $\sqrt{2} = \frac{a}{b}$, where a and b are relatively prime integers. Relatively prime integers are integers that have no common factor other than one, therefore $\frac{a}{b}$ is a fraction written in lowest terms. It is also this condition that provides the contradiction. If we square both sides of the equation, $\sqrt{2} = \frac{a}{b}$, we have $2 = \frac{a^2}{b^2}$. This is equivalent to $a^2 = 2b^2$. However, this says that x^2 is an even number, thus a is an even number. If a is even and $\frac{a^2}{b^2} = b^2$, b is also even. Thus a and b have a factor in common other than one, namely two, and are not relatively prime. Hence $\sqrt{2}$ is irrational.

The Rational Zero Theorem provides a direct proof method.

Exercises

1. Use the rational zero theorem to prove that $\sqrt{2}$ is irrational.

Consider $P(x) = x^2 - 2$. A known root of this polynomial is $\sqrt{2}$. But by the Rational Zero Theorem the only possible rational zeros are ±1 or ±2.

2. Show that the square of an even number is even.

Let a be even, $a = 2k$. Now $a^2 = 4k^2 = 2(2k^2)$, which is even.

3. Show that any integer zeros of a polynomial function must be factors of the constant term a_0.

Let $k = \frac{p}{q}$ be an integer where p is a factor of a_0 and q a factor of a_n. Therefore $a_0 = k(qM)$, for some M, and so k divides a_0.

6-8 Graphing Calculator Activity

Rational Root Theorem

The following program performs synthetic division and displays the depressed polynomial coefficients in rational form. The program will allow the testing of possible rational zeros of a polynomial function.

PROGRAM: SYNTHDIV

Disp "DEGREE OF DIVIDEND"	P+1→P
Input M	Disp "COEFFICIENT"
Disp "COEFFICIENTS?"	Input A
Disp "0=SAME"	A→L₁(P)
Disp "1=QUOTIENT"	If P<M+1
Disp "2=NEW"	Goto 1
Input U	Lbl 2
Disp "POSSIBLE ROOT"	1→P
Input R	0→S
If U=0	Lbl 3
Goto 2	L₁(P)→F
If U=1	F+S→Q
Goto 4	Disp Q ▶ Frac
0→P	Pause
Lbl 1	RQ→S

Q→L₂(P)	
P+1→P	
If P≤M+1	
Goto 3	
Stop	
Lbl 4	
0→P	
Lbl 5	
1+P→P	
L₁(P)→L₁(P)	
If P<M+1	
Goto 5	
Goto 2	

Example Find all of the rational zeros of $f(x) = 2x^3 - 11x^2 - 12x + 9$.

Use the program to test possible zeros. Test the zero 9 first.

Keystrokes: PRGM ▼ [SYNTHDIV] ENTER ENTER 3 ENTER 2 ENTER 1 ENTER 2 ENTER (-) 11 ENTER 12 ENTER 9 ENTER. Press ENTER until the screen displays Done.

```
POSSIBLE ROOT
?9
        -3/2
        3/4
        -3
Done
```

The column of numbers are the coefficients of the depressed polynomial. Since the last number is not zero, 9 is not a solution. Test −1. Press ENTER 3 ENTER. Choose 0 for the same coefficients. Press ENTER (-) 1 then ENTER until finished. Repeat this until a zero is found. Then press ENTER 2 for the degree of the depressed polynomial and ENTER 1 for the quotient.

The zeros are 3, 3, and $-\frac{1}{2}$.

Exercises

Find all the rational zeros of each function.

1. $f(x) = x^3 - 8x^2 - 23x + 30$ **1, −3, 10**

2. $f(x) = x^3 - 7x^2 + 2x + 40$ **−2, 4, 5**

3. $f(x) = 2x^3 - x^2 - 32x + 16$ **4, −4, $\frac{1}{2}$**

4. $f(x) = x^4 + x^3 - 11x^2 - 9x + 18$ **1, −2, 3, −3**

5. $p(x) = 3x^4 + 11x^3 + 11x^2 + x - 2$ **−1, −2, $-\frac{1}{3}$**

6. $p(x) = x^4 - 2x^3 + x^2 - 3x - 12$ **−1, 3**

7. $p(x) = 3x^5 + x^4 - 243x - 81$ **3, −3, $-\frac{1}{3}$**

8. $p(x) = 3x^4 + 13x^3 + 15x^2 - 4$ **−2**

Chapter 6 Assessment Answer Key

Quiz 1 (Lessons 6-1 and 6-2)
Page 57

1. $-24n^4y^7$
2. $8x^2y^2$
3. $12x^6 - 4x^5 + 3x^4 - 22x^3 + 7x^2 + 6x - 2$
4. $6x^2 + xy - 3y^2$
5. $9p + r$
6. $-3x + 3$
7. $8x^2 + 18x - 35$
8. A
9. $m - 3 + \dfrac{6}{m + 4}$
10. $a^2 - 3a + 1$

Quiz 2 (Lessons 6-3 and 6-4)
Page 57

1. 57
2. even; 2
3. between -1 and 0, between 1 and 2, between 3 and 4
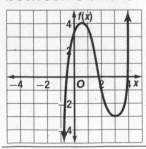
4. 2; 8
5. 0; 235

Quiz 3 (Lessons 6-5 and 6-6)
Page 58

1. $3(2a + 3)(a - 2)$
2. $-3, -\sqrt{5}, \sqrt{5}, 3$
3. C
4. 46; 277
5. $x + 2$; $x + 3$

Quiz 4 (Lessons 6-7 and 6-8)
Page 58

1. 3 or 1; 2 or 0; 4, 2, or 0
2. $3, 1 - i, 1 + i$
3. Sample answer: $f(x) = x^3 - 6x^2 + 10x - 8$
4. C
5. 6 ft × 9 ft × 10 ft

Mid-Chapter Test
Page 59

1. C
2. G
3. B
4. F
5. D
6. H
7. at $x = 1$, between -4 and -3 between -2 and -1
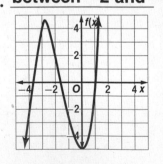
8. $2x^2 - 3x + 1$
9. $x^2 - 5x + 1 + \dfrac{2}{x + 7}$
10. $x^2 - 2x + 4$
11. $c^2 - c - 12$

Chapter 6 Assessment Answer Key

synthetic
1. substitution

2. relative maximum

3. quadratic form

4. simplify

5. synthetic division

6. standard notation

7. minimum

depressed
8. polynomial

9. leading coefficient

polynomial in one
10. variable

11. Sample answer:
The end behavior
of a graph is a
description of how
the graph behaves
when the value of x
becomes very small
or very large.

12. Sample answer:
The degree of a
polynomial is
the degree of the
monomial with
the greatest degree.

1. D

2. F

3. B

4. H

5. D

6. H

7. D

8. G

9. D

10. J

11. A

12. H

13. B

14. F

15. A

16. H

17. B

18. J

19. A

20. F

B: −12

Chapter 6 Assessment Answer Key

Form 2A
Page 63

Page 64

Page 66

1. __A__

2. __J__

3. __D__

4. __J__

5. __C__

6. __F__

7. __C__

8. __H__

9. __A__

10. __J__

11. __C__

12. __G__

13. __A__

14. __H__

15. __C__

16. __G__

17. __D__

18. __F__

19. __D__

20. __G__

B: __−41__

1. __A__

2. __H__

3. __A__

4. __J__

5. __C__

6. __H__

7. __C__

8. __F__

9. __C__

10. __F__

11. __D__

12. __F__

13. __B__

14. __G__

15. __C__

16. __G__

17. __C__

18. __F__

19. __B__

20. __F__
$(z + 3)(z - 3)$

B: $(x + 2y)(x - 2y)$

Chapter 6 Assessment Answer Key

1. $75r^4t^6$

2. $\dfrac{a^2c^4}{9b^6}$

3. $3c^2 - 14c + 12$

4. $6x^2 - 7x - 20$

5. $14p^2 + 3p - 12$

6. $24k^9 - 28k^7 - 12k^5 - 2k^4 + 3k^2$

7. $5x + 3.5(400 - x)$; $1.5x + 1400$

8. $5y^2 - 12y + 21 - \dfrac{73}{2y + 3}$

9. $x^2 + x - 20 + \dfrac{10}{x + 3}$

10. $(2x - 3y)(z + 4)$

11. -176

12. $x^2 - x - 3$

13. $f(x) \to +\infty$ as $x \to +\infty$; $f(x) \to +\infty$ as $x \to -\infty$

14. even

15. 4

Page 68

16. between -2 and -1, between 0 and 1, between 1 and 2

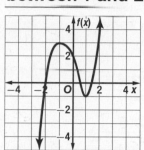

17. Sample answer: rel. max. at $x = -1$, rel. min. at $x = 1$

18. $9(n^3)^2 - 36(n^3)$

19. $\sqrt{15}, -\sqrt{15}, i\sqrt{3}, -i\sqrt{3}$

20. -3

21. $x + 3, x - 5$

22. 3 or 1; 1; 2 or 0

23. 14 in. × 8 in. × 15 in.

24. $\pm 1, \pm 2, \pm 4, \pm 8, \pm \dfrac{1}{2}$

25. $-2, 1, \dfrac{3}{2}$

B: $\dfrac{x - 6}{x - 4}$

Chapter 6 Assessment Answer Key

Form 2D
Page 69

Page 70

1. $\dfrac{40c^{13}d^2}{bc^2}$

2. $\dfrac{bc^2}{4a^4}$

3. $7f^2 - 2f + 3$

4. $10m^2 - 7m - 6$

5. $6g^3 - 3g^2 - 7g + 8$

6. $30k^5 + k^4 - 14k^3$

7. $7x + 4.5(500 - x);$
   $2.5x + 2250$

8. $4x^2 - 3x + 3 - \dfrac{7}{2x - 1}$

9. $x^2 + 6x + 3 + \dfrac{16}{x - 2}$

10. $(4x + y)(5x - 2)$

11. -134

12. $x^2 - 2x - 1$

13. $f(x) \to -\infty$ as $x \to +\infty;$
    $f(x) \to -\infty$ as $x \to -\infty$

14. even

15. 4

16. between -2 and -1,
    between -1 and 0,
    between 1 and 2

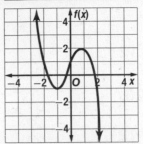

17. Sample answer:
    rel. max. at $x = 1$,
    rel. min. at $x = -1$

18. $5(x^5)^2 - 4(x^5) + 3$

19. $\sqrt{6}, -\sqrt{6}, i\sqrt{2}, -i\sqrt{2}$

20. 132

21. $x + 3, x + 1$

22. 2 or 0; 2 or 0;
    4, 2, or 0

23. 22 in. $\times$ 6 in. $\times$ 2 in.

24. $\pm 1, \pm 2, \pm 7, \pm 14,$
    $\pm\dfrac{1}{2}, \pm\dfrac{7}{2}$

25. $-3, \dfrac{2}{3}, 1$

B: $\dfrac{x + 4}{x + 5}$

Chapter 6 Assessment Answer Key

1. ____ a^2 ____

2. ____ $-5x^3y^2$ ____

3. ____ $12p^2 - \dfrac{5}{3}pr - \dfrac{16}{5}r^2$ ____

4. ____ $m^2 - 4mp + 4p^2$ ____

5. ____ $36k^8 - 13k^6 - 64k^4 + 30k^2$ ____

6. ____ $9x + 5.5(300 - x);$ $3.5x + 1650$ ____

7. ____ $x^2 + 3x + 9 + \dfrac{22x - 2}{x^2 - 3x + 1}$ ____

8. ____ $2x^2 - x + 1$ ____

9. ____ $2(9w^2 + n^2)(3w + n)$ $(3w - n)$ ____

10. ____ $(x^2 + 2y^2)$ $(x^4 - 2x^2y^2 + 4y^4)$ ____

11. ____ $\dfrac{\pm i\sqrt{105}}{3}$ ____

12. ____ $\dfrac{13}{3}$ ____

13. ____ $x^4 - 7x^2 - x$ ____

14. ____ $f(x) \to -\infty$ as $x \to -\infty$; $f(x) \to +\infty$ as $x \to +\infty$; odd; 4 ____

15. ____ between 0 and 1, between 1 and 2 ____

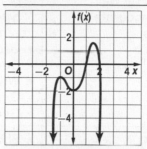

16. ____ Sample answer: rel. max. at $x = -1$ and $x = 1$, rel. min. at $x = 0$ ____

17. ____ $b[9(b^2)^2 + 3(b^2) - 8]$ ____

18. ____ 16, 81 ____

19. ____ 7014 ____

20. ____ -3 ____

21. ____ 5, 3, or 1; 5, 3, or 1; 8, 6, 4, 2, or 0 ____

22. ____ -1, 3, 3 $-2i$, 3 $+ 2i$ ____

23. ____ $\pm 1, \pm 3, \pm 5, \pm 15,$ $\pm\dfrac{1}{9}, \pm\dfrac{1}{3}, \pm\dfrac{5}{9}, \pm\dfrac{5}{3}$ ____

24. ____ $-\dfrac{1}{4}, -\dfrac{1}{2}, \dfrac{1}{3}, 2$ ____

25. ____ 4 meters ____

B: ____ 24 ____

Chapter 6 Assessment Answer Key

Page 73, Extended-Response Test
Scoring Rubric

Score	General Description	Specific Criteria
4	**Superior** A correct solution that is supported by well-developed, accurate explanations	• Shows thorough understanding of the concepts of operations with polynomials; *polynomial functions; graphing polynomial functions; determining number and type of roots of a polynomial equation; and finding rational zeros of a polynomial function.* • Uses appropriate strategies to solve problems. • Computations are correct. • Written explanations are exemplary. • Graphs are accurate and appropriate. • Goes beyond requirements of some or all problems.
3	**Satisfactory** A generally correct solution, but may contain minor flaws in reasoning or computation	• Shows an understanding of the concepts of operations with polynomials; *polynomial functions; graphing polynomial functions; determining number and type of roots of a polynomial equation; and finding rational zeros of a polynomial function.* • Uses appropriate strategies to solve problems. • Computations are mostly correct. • Written explanations are effective. • Graphs are mostly accurate and appropriate. • Satisfies all requirements of problems.
2	**Nearly Satisfactory** A partially correct interpretation and/or solution to the problem	• Shows an understanding of most of the concepts of operations with polynomials; *polynomial functions; graphing polynomial functions; determining number and type of roots of a polynomial equation; and finding rational zeros of a polynomial function.* • May not use appropriate strategies to solve problems. • Computations are mostly correct. • Written explanations are satisfactory. • Graphs are mostly accurate. • Satisfies the requirements of most of the problems.
1	**Nearly Unsatisfactory** A correct solution with no supporting evidence or explanation	• Final computation is correct. • No written explanations or work is shown to substantiate the final computation. • Graphs may be accurate but lack detail or explanation. • Satisfies minimal requirements of some of the problems.
0	**Unsatisfactory** An incorrect solution indicating no mathematical understanding of the concept or task, or no solution is given	• Shows little or no understanding of most of the concepts of operations with polynomials; *polynomial functions; graphing polynomial functions; determining number and type of roots of a polynomial equation; and finding rational zeros of a polynomial function.* • Does not use appropriate strategies to solve problems. • Computations are incorrect. • Written explanations are unsatisfactory. • Graphs are inaccurate or inappropriate. • Does not satisfy requirements of problems. • No answer may be given.

Chapter 6 Assessment Answer Key

Page 73, Extended-Response Test
Sample Answers

In addition to the scoring rubric found on page A32, the following sample answers may be used as guidance in evaluating open-ended assessment items.

1a. The length and width are $2x + 1$ and $x + 1$ units.

1b. The perimeter can be found using the formula $p = 2(l + w)$. Substituting $2x + 1$ for length and $x + 1$ for width,
$$p = 2(2x + 1 + x + 1)$$
$$= 2(3x + 2) = 6x + 4$$

1c. For $x = 3$, the length is 7 units, the width is 4 units, the perimeter is 22 units, and the area is 28 units^2. The value of x must be chosen so that the length, width, perimeter, and area are all positive. The expressions $2x + 1$, $x + 1$, $6x + 4$, and $2x^2 + 3x + 1$ will all be positive only if $x > -\frac{1}{2}$.

1d. $2x^2 + 3x + 1 = (2x + 1)(x + 1)$

Students should indicate that the factors of the polynomial are the same as the dimensions of the rectangle in part **a**.

2a. and b. Students must sketch a polynomial function having exactly 5 zeros, opposite end behavior, 2 relative maxima, and 2 relative minima, labeled as shown.

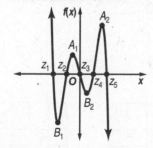

2c. Regardless of the function sketched, D: all real numbers and R: all real numbers.

2d. Students must state either "As $x \to +\infty$, $f(x) \to -\infty$ and as $x \to -\infty$, $f(x) \to +\infty$" (as for the sample function shown) or "As $x \to +\infty$, $f(x) \to +\infty$ and as $x \to -\infty$, $f(x) \to -\infty$."

3a. Answers must be of the form
$$P(x) = a_0x^4 + a_1x^3 + a_2x^2 + a_3x + a_4,$$
where $a_n \neq 0$ for any n. Sample answer: $P(x) = x^4 + x^3 + x^2 + 2x + 3$.

3b. Students should show by direct substitution, and by synthetic substitution, how to find $P(-2)$. For the sample function in **a**, $P(-2) = 11$.

3c. Students should indicate that $x + 1$ is a factor of $P(x)$ if and only if $P(-1) = 0$. For the sample function in **a**, $P(-1) = 2 \neq 0$, so $x + 1$ is not a factor of $P(x)$.

3d. Students should use Descartes' Rule of Signs to determine the number of positive and negative real zeros of $P(x)$. For the sample function in **a**, $P(x)$ has no positive real zeros and has 4, 2 or 0 negative real zeros.

3e. Students must explain that any rational zeros of $P(x)$ must be of the form $\frac{p}{q}$, where p is a factor of a_4 and q is a factor of a_0. For the sample function in **a**, $a_0 = 1$ and $a_4 = 3$, so the only possible rational zeros are ± 1 and ± 3.

3f. For each of the possible rational zeros z_n found in part **e**, students must show whether $x - z_n$ is a factor of $P(x)$. For the sample function in **a**, there are no rational zeros.

Answers

Chapter 6 Assessment Answer Key

1. Ⓐ Ⓑ Ⓒ ●

2. Ⓕ Ⓖ ● Ⓙ

3. Ⓐ Ⓑ ● Ⓓ

4. Ⓕ Ⓖ Ⓗ ●

5. Ⓐ ● Ⓒ Ⓓ

6. Ⓕ ● Ⓗ Ⓙ

7. Ⓐ ● Ⓒ Ⓓ

8. Ⓕ Ⓖ Ⓗ ●

9. Ⓐ Ⓑ Ⓒ ●

10. Ⓕ ● Ⓗ Ⓙ

11. Ⓐ Ⓑ Ⓒ ●

12. Ⓕ Ⓖ ● Ⓙ

13. ● Ⓑ Ⓒ Ⓓ

14. Ⓕ ● Ⓗ Ⓙ

15. ● Ⓑ Ⓒ Ⓓ

16. 512

17. 150

Chapter 6 Assessment Answer Key

Standardized Test Practice
Page 76

18. $(n + 3)^2$

19. $a^2 - 7a + 10$

20. $y = -x + 4$

21. $(3, -2)$

22. $s \geq 0; t \geq 0;$
$3s + 4t \leq 500;$
$s + t \leq 150$

23. 3×2

24. $\begin{bmatrix} 25 \\ -29 \end{bmatrix}$

25. $\begin{bmatrix} 3 & -2 \\ 4 & 5 \end{bmatrix} \cdot \begin{bmatrix} m \\ f \end{bmatrix} = \begin{bmatrix} 16 \\ 9 \end{bmatrix}$

26. 1.5×10^{11}

27. $3x^2 - x + 1 - \dfrac{1}{2x + 1}$

28a. 4

28b. 2

28c. $73; 162a^4 - 27a^3$
$+ 54a^2 - 21a - 5$